The Bible tells us of . . . .
Science spells out . . . .

The author's religious [beliefs]
is sincere; his scientific
facts are sound, thorough, and
presented so lay readers can
understand them.

I have great respect for what he has
attempted to do in this book.

Some of his conclusions and the arguments
to back them up seem forced,
contrived — esp. in the earlier
chapters. I believe the book improves
as it moves along, and therefore
recommend that the ~~p~~ reader
persevere.

[Any person who wants to recognize the
authority of the Bible and also
accept ~~the~~ findings of modern
science should benefit from this book]

THE GENESIS ANSWER

This Book
has been presented to the
CHURCH LIBRARY

of ___FUMC___

___Georgetown___

_____

by ___Dr. Marten King___

THE GENESIS ANSWER

THE GENESIS ANSWER

A Scientist's Testament for Divine Creation

WILLIAM LEE STOKES

PRENTICE-HALL, INC., Englewood Cliffs, New Jersey 07632

Library of Congress Catalog Card Number: 83-63359

Cover photograph: The Vela Supernova Remnant
Photography by David Malin of the Anglo-Australian
Observatory, and Photolabs, Royal Observatory, Edinburgh.
Original negatives by UK Schmidt Telescope Unit.
Copyright © Royal Observatory, Edinburgh.

Printed in the United States of America

10   9   8   7   6   5   4   3   2   1

ISBN   0-13-350976-1

Prentice-Hall International, Inc., London
Prentice-Hall of Australia Pty. Limited, Sydney
Editora Prentice-Hall do Brasil, Ltda., Rio de Janeiro
Prentice-Hall Canada Inc., Toronto
Prentice-Hall of India Private Limited, New Delhi
Prentice-Hall of Japan, Inc., Tokyo
Prentice-Hall of Southeast Asia Pte. Ltd., Singapore
Whitehall Books Limited, Wellington, New Zealand

CONTENTS

5915

PREFACE

The Mosaic account of creation has probably been read by more men and women than any other literary work. I use this phraseology to make certain that the Christian Bible, Jewish Torah, and Islamic Koran are included. Moses is a certified prophet and major contributor to the sacred scripture of all who profess to be Christians, Jews, or Moslems. As an indispensable introduction to the Bible and Torah, the works of Moses have been translated into practically all languages and are thus available to almost all who wish to consult them.

For centuries the Book of Genesis was the final and sufficient word on the origin of all things. The only alternative was the primitive creation myths of the times obviously fashioned by human beings. The Genesis account is dignified, brief, and confident. Its permanent preservation and wide dissemination were assured by the coercive influence of Christianity and Judaism.

With the passage of time and the blossoming of science the grip of religion was loosened and bit by bit the authority of the creation scriptures eroded away. The transition from a scripture-dominated to a science-dominated view of the cosmos was protracted and painful. The Copernican Revolution seriously damaged ecclesiastical authority, and introduction of the idea of natural selection by Charles Darwin caused a rift that persists today. The weakening of biblical authority furnished the excuse to break away from oppressive religious influences that many had been looking for. Those who remained true to the faith did so either by ignoring Darwin or by denouncing him as a dedicated evildoer. There were a few, rightfully called Christian Darwinists, who took the time and effort to think the matter through. They found the process of biological evolution compatible with and even supportive of their views of Christianity. Their arguments might have persuaded even Darwin had he lived to hear them out.

As it was, the Christian Darwinists went practically unnoticed. Their arguments were too devious for ordinary citizens, who preferred the more clearcut and exciting polemics of extremists on either side. The issue became one of choosing between evolution or Christianity. The question in most minds was and still is: Did the human race get here by evolution or creation? Stated thus, there is no possible middle ground, and since neither side has been willing to compromise, the conflict has continued for a full century without basic change. At the present time evolutionists and creationists confront each other over issues plainly indicated by their respective names. Creationists, claiming to represent all those who believe in literal scripture, are insisting on a "week" of creation only a few thousand years ago.

Recent legal action seeking equal time for creationist views in the public schools has provoked a flood of books by aroused scientists. Under ordinary circumstances the content of these books would have effectively discredited most creationist arguments, but religious issues are at stake and emotion outweighs logic. No amount of factual evidence will convince dedicated believers to give up their Bibles. Scientific arguments seem destined to fail because they are perceived as atheistic by dedicated religionists and because they are written by scientists for other scientists in language the average reader cannot understand.

After decades of stalemate new and powerful influences are taking effect. The past few decades have brought truly revolutionary discoveries in science that cannot be ignored by anyone, especially the creationists. Physics is on the verge of elucidating the basic nature of matter and energy. Astronomy has integrated an evolving universe of big bangs, spinning galaxies, and black holes. Geology has been completely revolutionized by the concept of slowly moving crustal plates. Concurrently, the application of geological techniques to the study of other solid bodies of the solar system has revealed similarities and differences of inestimable significance in reconstructing the history of the earth and solar system. In biology the discovery of DNA and the mechanisms of inheritance and variation has completely revitalized thinking about how living things operate. Finally, in anthropology there have been more important discoveries in the last fifteen years than in all previous time.

These great discoveries have suddenly elevated science from a largely descriptive level into the realm of historical synthesis. Almost in unison the sciences are converging on questions of origin (creation). As great space age discoveries are being integrated into the fund of general knowledge, creationists are becoming increasingly insistent that Genesis requires the bringing forth of all things in six twenty-four hour days about six thousand years ago. Never have the grounds of conflict been more clearly defined. Never have the facts on which to base a decision been more plentiful.

Curiosity clearly outweighs necessity as a motive for space age exploration. The chief incentive to reach the moon, to analyze the Martian environment for signs of life, to build expensive space telescopes, and to equip listening devices for receiving intelligent messages from extraterrestrial sources has been the hope of proving that we are not alone. The cost has been immense but there have been no serious objections to continuing the search for the origins of the universe, earth, life, and the human race.

So far results have been negative. It may be that we will never positively know more than one universe, one habitable planet, one expression of life, and one humankind. Nevertheless, the contributions to knowledge have been unprecedented. More important perhaps is the degree to which scientific methods and modes of thinking have penetrated the consciousness of all levels of the citizenry. This sharing of the great adventure of space exploration will be a critical factor in what lies ahead.

As if to compensate for the depressing thought that we are isolated and alone, there has been a veritable outpouring of fictional substitutes. Our fantasy makers have proceeded to populate the realms of space and time that are forever beyond our reach. It cannot be without significance that the most successful science-fiction movies, books, and television plots include quests, searches, and cosmic contests between good and evil forces.

Matching in magnitude the crowds that flock to be entertained by space age fantasies are those who gather to hear popular evangelists dispense their different versions about the present state and future of humankind. Needless to say that those who listen are also hoping for messages from other realms, for assurances that life has a meaning and for consolation in the face of what seems to be impending disaster.

The question of the age is whether the human race is here as a result of meaningless accident or by divine benevolent intent. As yet the answer is uncertain. Science does not claim to be seeking God but cold rational research has made his existence an undeniable alternative: Either we are here by a series of improbable coincidences or by supernatural interventions. We come face to face with this crucial choice now that we know the earth and its inhabitants are highly unusual, if not actually unique. Having gotten along very well without invoking supernatural influences, scientists are not inclined to call on God even at this critical stage. Their obstinacy puzzles and infuriates religious people who are losing faith in the ability of science to deal with basic issues. Just as too much dogmatic theology in the middle ages gave rise to science, so today too much dogmatic science is giving rise to a religious resurgence.

How is theology reacting now that it has the opportunity to deal with problems of origin raised by science? There are almost as many reactions as there are sects. Many of the traditional old line churches have accepted the dictate of science that the creation scriptures are not to be taken as a textbook of geology, biology, and astronomy. As the old-line churches have declined, the "third force" of fundamentalist and evangelical groups has grown in influence. Some of these ignore the problem of reconciliation with science, and others have it as a matter of doctrine that the scriptures are literally true no matter what science may say. This has reached a state of militant assertiveness as creationists, acting as self-appointed representatives of all Christian churches, attack every actual or perceived weakness or mistake of science.

The average person, not being trained in either science or theology, is called upon to choose between two alleged sources of truth, divine revelation and scientific inquiry. Science seems to be telling him there is no god, while theology asks him to believe in a god who chose to create a universe full of nonsensical contradictions and endless deceptions. It is more than ironic that modern persons in this informed and sophisticated age are unable to reconcile the intellectual and spiritual facts of their existence to produce the happiness to which they are entitled.

Those who understand the facts of science are numerically insignificant compared to the vast majority who depend on others for their opinions and who act mainly from emotion or instinct. As a scientist my basic reaction is to answer the creationists with unemotional, devastating factual arguments. But I have procrastinated and my colleagues have done the job in great style; there must be a dozen books giving updated scientific arguments. My experience through several decades of teaching historical geology on an elementary cultural level has convinced me that the uninformed majority needs and deserves more than technical arguments. Educators apparently have nothing to substitute for that which they are eliminating. Too often I have seen alert questioning youngsters who undertook their grade school dinosaur projects with great enthusiasm transformed into apathetic college students resisting all efforts to convince them that the study of nature should be a personal lifelong soul-satisfying, faith-promoting adventure.

There will always be a vast number of teenagers required to

study science to win their diplomas. The national welfare needs citizens who understand basic science. Legal means will be found to teach it to them, and funds will be extracted to provide whatever is needed. All this is well and good but there are ominous obstacles ahead. How can science be taught so as to meet the approval of parents and school boards who do not want to hear about evolution or who think it unfair not to include the traditional biblical version of creation? Who will write and publish text books satisfactory to both creationists and evolutionists? And can we honestly expect our young people to deal with questions that their teachers cannot explain and their parents do not understand!

Decades of well-intended efforts to thoroughly compartmentalize church and state and to keep God out of public classrooms has left us in an educational quagmire. According to the best opinion surveys a majority of Americans believe the Bible to be divinely inspired, and millions consider it to be literal word for word *truth*. It is perplexing to understand how these literal believers reconcile their opinions about scripture with the outpouring of evidence from daily newspapers and televisions broadcasts that such opinions are contrary to the findings of science.

Scientists are convinced they are right but as long as their findings appear to be contrary to the scripture all their arguments are in vain. I realize this but am convinced that we can have both our scriptures and our science. I also realize that my efforts are wasted unless I get my message to those who need it most. Classified as I must be as a practicing scientist, college professor, and believer in evolution, how can I hope to gain the attention of those to whom scientists, college professors, and evolutionists appear as enemies? I am confident in the hope that my readers will include men and women of good will who can accept my interpretations for the truth that is in them and assure their followers that I have violated neither the spirit of the scriptures nor the facts of science. Truth must make its own way.

Obviously I am not a trained theologian. But I can read and ponder the creation scriptures and I am convinced that my worldly scientific background has aided me in understanding their meaning. The scriptures are for everyone, not merely for a relatively few scholars. Perhaps part of our problem is that the majority has let the minority do their reading and thinking for them. I build my arguments around the familiar words, phrases, and verses of Genesis 1 and 2. My text is available for checking by anyone who has a Bible. Although my science is not as simple, I do make reference to well known natural things such as earth, water, plants, animals, planets, stars, and galaxies. By this approach I feel confident that readers at any level will understand enough about space age science to appreciate my basic points. Few people today are unaware of the variety, beauty, and majesty of what has been discovered in space. And who does not have access to museums with dinosaurs and other exhibits pertaining to the earth and its past life. Perhaps the million-year eras of geologists and the light years of astronomers are incomprehensible, but who except dedicated creationists would want to argue about the possibility of their meaning?

Certainly, the level of information of today's citizens is far above that of our ancestors of only a few generations ago who believed in a flat earth circled by stars set in movable transparent spheres. I am optimistic, too, that my readers are ready to be persuaded that the creator of the universe has had the wisdom to send a message understandable and comforting not only to those of a less sophisticated flat-earth age but consoling and believable also to their space age descendants.

For believers in the Mosaic account of creation I bring the good news that they are vindicated in their belief in a god who not only created all things but also inspired and preserved a reliable account of creation in his scriptures. To scientists and believers in science, the good news is that their facts and well-founded theories are true. The bad news for Bible believers is that they must substitute space age interpretations for the time-honored but impossible traditions of the past. The bad news for scientists is that they cannot safely deny divine creative influences in the early history of the universe. They can possess the seventh day if they are willing to relinquish something of the previous six. Everyone wins and everyone loses; compromise seems to be the best solution.

My task is to prove that the seven days of creation are not mere allegorical stages, not clever literary devices, and certainly not ordinary twenty-four hour intervals. The first six days are clearly defined as periods consisting, as does the Jewish sabbath, of an evening and a morning or, in other words, an interval of darkness and an interval of light. The seventh day is different in that no light and dark stages are specified. It began with the watering of the earth and has not yet ended. This is the Genesis Code: Each creative "day" consists of a period dominated by darkness and a period dominated by light. Earth emerged from chaos as a product of the progressive succession of six such periods. The creative days were not of equal duration and were not intended to be measures of time. They are not the periods, epochs, and eras invented by geologists. Their meaning is celestial and not terrestrial. They are God's divisions of his own creation. When we fully recognize them for what they are we will comprehend the meaning of the creation scriptures.

Salt Lake City, Utah   William Lee Stokes

THE CHALLENGE
AND MYSTERY
OF THE CREATION SCRIPTURES

The Holy Bible is the world's all-time, best-selling book and has been translated into almost every human language. There must surely be more Bibles in existence than any other written work. Even if most copies have remained unopened and unread the Bible is still the world's most studied book. It is a composite work of many parts not all of which have equal status and value. The Old Testament portion has been in existence much longer and is a part of the sacred writings of far more people than is the New Testament. The first five books of the Old Testament known as the Pentateuch, the Law or the Torah constitute the basis of the Jewish religion. Many other books, written as commentaries and explanations of the laws of Moses have been produced by the Jews.

For several reasons the Book of Genesis is the most studied of the thirty-six writings that make up the Old Testament. Obviously, since Genesis comes first, it has been read by practically all of those whose good intentions were to complete the entire Bible but may have failed at various stages to continue the task. In the second place Genesis has more than its share of the ever-popular, sacred stories that Christians and Jews include in their standard courses of indoctrination and instruction. Finally, it is the basic document of the Creation, a theme considered by most

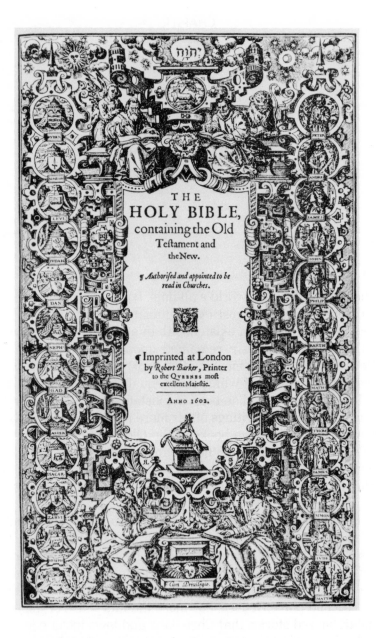

Fig. 1-1   The title page of the Bishops' Bible printed in London, 1602. On the left side are symbols for the twelve tribes of Israel; on the right the twelve apostles are depicted.

Christians to be second in importance only to the redemptive mission of Jesus Christ.

Quite possibly no written statement in the literature of mankind has been subject to more study than the first two chapters of Genesis. The slightly more than 1400 words making up the 56 arbitrary verses in the King James Version and their equivalent in other versions and translations have been scanned by countless millions of casual readers in search of nothing more than their Sunday School gold stars, perused deeply by countless devout believers searching for solace and assurance, dissected by hundreds of scholars looking for new or hidden meanings and combed over by infidels and enemies of religion for reasons helpful to their various causes.

It is worth emphasizing that scripture reading is one of the most time-honored pursuits of literate men. Dating as it does from the time of Moses, the Book of Genesis has been available in one form or another for over three thousand years. There is good evidence that many had access to it even in ancient times. The writer of Ecclesiastes was led to exclaim long before Christ: "Of the making of many books there is no end." Among the many books of ancient times the works of Moses must have had a prominent place.

The Genesis account is not the only explanation of how things came into being. Myths and legends of creation are part of the folklore of every culture. That most of these stories are products of human imagination is perfectly clear. The Biblical account is not so easily disposed of; its brevity, dignity, simplicity, and comprehensiveness place it in a class by itself. Topics treated in the creation scriptures are fundamental and have been debated for centuries not only by those who accept the Bible as holy writ but also by those who may never have heard of Hebrew scriptures as such.

Scripture affirms the creative role of God in the bringing forth of all things and gives reason for the uniqueness of man. However, the Bible is not man's only witness; the natural world also inspires belief in a supreme being. The findings of science, in the mind of the average man, constitute compelling evidence of a benevolent creator. Two lines of evidence for the same thing should be stronger than one and together they should be invincible. Ironically this has not proven to be the case. Instead of bringing harmony among religious men and widespread reverence for God there has resulted an age-long controversy generally known as the conflict between science and theology.

The history of attempted reconciliation between the scriptural account of creation and the findings of science has been a painful story of intellectual frustration. The desire to believe in both sources of evidence has been hampered by both scriptural and scientific interpretations that appear to be hopelessly illogical, impossible and contradictory. Plainly the supreme being, whose awe-inspiring works are manifest in nature, cannot be, in the minds of most men, the God of Genesis and certainly not Jesus Christ of the New Testament who calls sinful men to repentance and all to moral responsibility. The God of Nature and God of the Bible remain unreconciled and apart.

The average, thinking person who sincerely wishes to believe in a supreme being is trapped between two seemingly infallible sources of truth, scientific fact and divine revelation. The spokesmen for each side seem well informed and unshakable in their beliefs. How can the common man question either side and how can he choose between them? Many have obviously chosen science as the destined winner. This includes not only most scientists but also many theologians. Even the most zealous fundamentalists have had to bend here and there as Bryan did at the Scopes trial. Science is taught with power and authority at all educational levels and the programs and projects of scientists are blessed with vast sums from the public treasury. The past performance of science seems to justify this admiration and support. The wonders and triumphs of science pour forth daily to become the common knowledge of every man. The products of science and technology have passed the stage of being niceties and luxuries; they are now absolute necessities without which civilization could not exist.

Contrary to what one might believe from current events the victory of science is far from complete. Just as religion seems to have spawned anti-religion so science may be giving rise to anti-science. Under the surface powerful counter currents are gathering force. Modern civilized man, faced with restrictions and shortages, can visualize dark days ahead and he can find reason to criticize science as being in part responsible. There is less confidence now that greater technical knowledge is capable of bringing happiness to the individual or of saving the race from a miserable doom. It is not surprising that the present is a time of religious revival. That 90 percent of Americans should declare faith in God and four out of ten of them believe that the Bible is literal word-for-word truth has implications that religion, far from being dead, is alive and growing. But it is not the traditional old-line organized churches that are recovering from their long

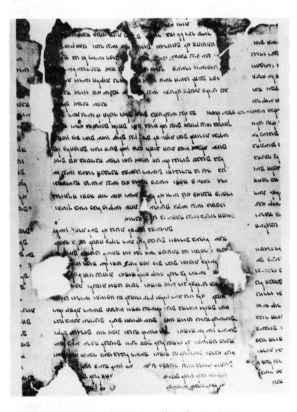

Fig. 1-2   A portion of the Dead Sea Scrolls. These timeworn records survived for over 2,000 years in dry caves near the Dead Sea. All but a few of the books of the Bible are represented in collections from these caves.

(Courtesy of Ralene Levy, Information Officer, Consulate General of Israel in New York.)

decline, rather it is the newer evangelical and fundamentalist sects that are showing the greatest vitality.

The new religious stirrings are definitely Bible-oriented. Popular evangelists who appear regularly on radio and television do their preaching with scriptures in hand and the so-called Bible Belt is where their cause prospers. Possibly more people are reading and believing the Bible than ever before.

The present religious situation is difficult to explain or describe. The ancient issues that stirred intellectual turmoil in the past have not been resolved and are, if anything, more pressing than ever. The problems of the existence or non-existence of God and the veracity of the Holy Bible can scarcely be described as trivial. In the past the common people left the solution of these problems up to their religious and secular leaders; now they seek to know for themselves on a personal basis. An amazing 34 percent of those questioned in a recent (1976) Gallup poll claim to have had a personal "born again" experience when they committed themselves to Jesus Christ.

What then has become of the science-theology controversy? It has not simply gone away—the basic problem of interpreting the creation scriptures remains unsolved and two opposing forces under the banners of Creationism and Evolutionism clearly exist. Nevertheless, active combat seems to be at a low ebb. Confrontations have been minor since the battle of the Scopes trial. Results seem invariably the same: science wins with a multitude of facts, theology loses with too many outmoded and unreasonable interpretations.

Even though Creationists will not admit defeat and scientists appear to have lost interest in fighting, nothing has really been settled. What prevails is a state of wary avoidance, weary apathy and noncommunication. An uneasy truce prevails as science refrains from trying to convince theology of its errors and theology leaves science to go its misguided godless way. The need for reconciliation is greater than ever. The split between science and theology that has widened since the time of Galileo must be counted as a major historical tragedy. It sent the heart and mind in different directions and robbed man of the unity he needs to attain the happier existence to which he is entitled. But reconciliation appears to be impossible. The experience of those who attempted it in the 17th and 18th centuries has discouraged almost all theologians and scientists from further efforts. Perhaps the middle road is not closed. It is well to remember that earlier thinkers who traversed it had but a small fraction of the information that exists today. Perhaps instead of making recon-

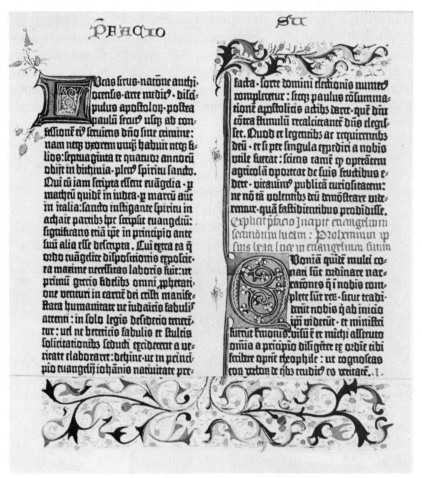

Fig. 1-3   Part of a page from the Gutenberg Bible. This great work came off the press of Johann Gutenberg of Mainz in the Rhineland, Germany, in 1456 and was the first book to be reproduced from movable type. Following this famous edition uncounted millions of Bibles in over 600 languages have been printed.

ciliation more difficult new knowledge has eased the way. Certainly the cure for error and misunderstanding is more truth—and we have more truth than ever before.

The time has come for science to demonstrate that it seeks for and builds on promising hypotheses and pursues truth wherever it leads. Likewise theology must be willing to prove that it too holds truth in highest regard and is the enemy of error wherever it is found. But there can be no understanding, no reconciliation and no vindication of truth without some very fundamental changes of attitude. It is a reproach to man's intelligence and wisdom that a fundamental schism exists between his intellectual and spiritual experience. The challenge of the times is to heal this division with any and all remedies at our command.

> Upon this gifted age, in its dark hour,
> Rains from the sky a meteoric shower
> Of facts . . . they lie unquestioned,
> > uncombined.
> Wisdom enough to leech us of our ill
> Is daily spun; but there exists no loom
> To weave it into fabric.

> Edna St. Vincent Millay
> *Collected Sonnets*

COMMENTS AND REFERENCES

The scope of human history is so vast that few minds can comprehend more than small segments of it. Mostly history is studied in bits and pieces restricted to certain time spans, peoples, or political entities. Comprehensive surveys include the time-honored *Outline of History* by H. G. Wells; *The Story of Mankind* by Hendrick W. Van Loon; and the epoch-marking, 11-volume *The Story of Civilization* by Will and Ariel Durant. These summaries are sufficient to substantiate the major points of this chapter. More about individual personalities and events as, for instance, Aristotle or the Dark Ages, can be found in specific books or articles. As a general rule, standard encyclopedias such as the *Encyclopaedia Britannica* and *Encyclopaedia Americana* carry concise, unbiased, and scholarly articles on all significant aspects of history. There are also a number of encyclopedias that cover human knowledge from narrower denominational viewpoints; these are found only in larger libraries.

Books dealing with the growth of scientific ideas about the universe are Alexander Koyre, 1957, *From the Closed World to the Infinite Universe*, John Hopkins; Arthur Koestler, 1963, *The Sleepwalkers*, Grosset and Dunlap; W. C. Dampier, 1966, *A History of Science and its Relations with Philosophy and Religion*, Cambridge; C. A. Coulson, 1958, *Science and Christian Belief*, Collins; George Sarton, 1970, *A History of Science*, Harvard University Press; and Sir Alan Cottrell, 1977, *Portrait of Nature: the World as Seen by Modern Science*, Scribners.

An account of the gradual decline of theological influences on students of natural science is John C. Greene, 1959, *The Death of Adam*, Mentor Books. Dealing more specifically with geological controversies is C. C. Gillispie, 1959, *Genesis and Geology*, Harper and Row. The subtitle identifies Gillispie's book as an account of the impact of scientific discoveries upon religious beliefs in the decades before Darwin.

Probably the best brief review of the intellectual progress and development of mankind is J. Bronowski, 1973, *The Ascent of Man*, Little, Brown and Co. This excellent book has been adapted for a 13-part television program that has been viewed by millions. A list of recommended readings may be obtained from stations showing the series.

PROVE ALL THINGS . . .

The creation scriptures are undeniably controversial. Over the centuries they have generated belief, doubt, and differences of opinion. To some they have been faith-promoting, to others faith-destroying, always a challenge, ever an enigma. Could it be that these scriptures are intended to present another opportunity for the exercise of faith? Genesis by itself is not sufficient to win believers but neither is it sufficient to turn them away. Perhaps it is not far from the truth to say that in the present age of science most of those who believe in the Old Testament do so in spite of Genesis rather than because of it. The difficulties that face traditional literal interpretations have grown with time until they seem insurmountable. A list of the less trivial and more widely expressed arguments against the creation scriptures must include at least the following:

1. It is impossible for any human writer or writers to have knowledge of the prehistory of the earth or the development of the universe before these subjects had been investigated scientifically.

2. There are apparently two conflicting accounts of creation, one in the first chapter of Genesis, the other in the second chapter. These differ in emphasis and in the order of the creative events. Although there appears to be a transition between the two accounts in the first few verses of Genesis 2 these verses make

little sense and could be nothing more than a clumsy attempt to fuse material from two different sources.

3.   Certain elements of the Genesis account are found in creation-myths of non-Hebraic people. These stories involve episodes and personalities that are difficult to accept as anything but human inventions. Genesis might thus be only a more cleverly contrived but still human account of how things came to be.

4.   If taken literally the story is that the totality of material things was brought into being in six 24-hour days about 6,000 years ago. Even though other scriptures are sometimes cited to possibly lengthen the creative days to 1,000 years each this is not convincing. How can this "quick creation" interpretation be reconciled with good evidence that the earth is billions of years old and the universe many times older?

5.   Although the Genesis account is clearly sequential and tells of 6 creative periods, these cannot be reconciled with the recognized epochs, periods, or eras of geologic history. Geologists have given up trying to correlate the record of scripture with the record of the rocks. Since science appears to have overwhelming factual evidence to support a version of the history of the earth that is at variance with the Genesis story, it is the scriptures that must be in error.

6.   The implication is that God created living things directly from non-living material most probably from the soil or ground. Since there were only six short creative days available there is no time for the evolutionary process which most students find reasonably in accord with the facts.

7.   The fact that plant life is mentioned as having been created on the third day before the appearance of the sun on the fourth day. How can plants possibly exist without sunlight?

8.   The statement that sun, moon and stars came into being after the earth, something entirely out of harmony with astronomical evidence that stars are of various ages — new ones are continually being created and some are many times older than the earth.

9.   The implication is that each and every living thing was commanded to multiply "its own kind" endlessly with no possi-

Fig. 2-1 Artist's concept of National Aeronautics and Space Administration's Space Telescope in operation 300 miles above the Earth's surface. It will be launched from the Space Shuttle depicted to the right below it. Since this telescope operates above the disturbing effects of the atmosphere it will enable astronomers to gaze several times further into space than ever before and to obtain images more than 10 times fainter than those taken from the ground. With it astronomers will observe some 350 times the volume of space that can now be seen. In astronomical terms it can search for planets around distant stars, examine supernova remnants and white dwarf stars, look at objects and events as they existed many billions of years ago, permit better study of multiple star systems and monitor the atmospheres and surfaces of solid objects in the solar system on which landings are planned.

This great instrument, culminating product of modern science and technology, may possibly reveal the edges of the visible universe and will certainly tell us much about events that produced the solar system and earth. (Courtesy NASA.)

bility of one species giving rise to another. Again there is conflict with the doctrine of organic evolution. Incidentally, no provision or explanation is given for extermination or for fossils.

10. The assertion that the first woman, Eve, was made from a rib of the first man, Adam.

A parallel list of reasons for believing in Genesis might include the following. This list can be no more fair, accurate or complete than the previous one. It is chiefly an index of what many believers consider important.

1. The entire scripture is the word of God, and Genesis, being an integral part of the Bible, cannot be excluded from a place of authority and respect.

2. Jesus Christ referred to the writings of Moses with favor, thus putting a stamp of divine approval on Genesis.

3. The fundamental message of Genesis—that God is the Creator—is compatible with the entirety of the Bible.

4. The wording of Genesis is dignified, simple, confident, positive and straightforward with no extraneous or extravagant explanations, interpolations or apologies.

5. The Genesis account affirms one God (or one Godhead) and is free from the bizarre, multiple, contentious personalities of most creation myths.

6. The human beings depicted in Genesis are believable persons with the strengths and weaknesses of ordinary mortals. They have no semi-supernatural traits or aberrations of character such as mark most mythological beings.

7. The events of Genesis are sequential and cumulative and the sequence is what would be expected in any orderly progressive or evolving system. The creation is all-inclusive.

8. The creations mentioned in Genesis, both animate and inanimate, are derived from that which precedes them; they do not have existence in a vacuum.

9. No evidence has been found to certify a human origin for the creation scriptures—the alleged authorship of God has not been refuted.

10.   The preservation of the wording and spirit of the creation story through centuries of translations and transcriptions bespeaks divine guidance as well as human integrity.

Comparison of these two lists emphasize a predictable fact: if a person believes in God he is automatically predisposed to accept the scriptures or be willing to make excuses for their shortcomings. Conversely, if one does not believe in God quite naturally he is less likely to accept supernatural elements in the scriptures. To be noted also among the objections is the predominance of items that are matters of factual nature while in the believers list matters of feeling or emotion are emphasized. This could be translated to mean that since most objections to the creation scriptures are of a factual nature they can be either proven or disproven by additional facts. This indeed seems to be born out historically; science which leans heavily on facts has yielded little that seems to support literal interpretations and much that disproves them. Scientists of the 18th and 19th centuries tried valiantly but unsuccessfully to reconcile Genesis with natural history but have now largely abandoned the attempt.

Fortunately, there are many who are unwilling to reject Genesis because it seems to fail in the face of the facts of science. They remain convinced that it has value as an assertion of the personality of God and his relation to man and the universe. Yet, in order to maintain their faith they must ignore much that is plainly stated or relegate these riddles to the realm of myth or allegory. But these believers are on the right road. Not the least important purpose of the creation scriptures is to prove that God is God and is the Creator of all that is. How better to demonstrate this than to make it unmistakably plain that he, God, indeed knows the end from the beginning? Significant also is the revelation that this foreknowledge need not be verified from hidden scrolls or secret caves. It has been there all along in the Bible for any man to read and ponder.

Even more to be marveled at is the fact that the message, though cryptic and obscure, is neither a lie nor a deception. It is not a complex allegory too deep to fathom and figurative phrases are rare. No one word or phrase describes the creation scriptures, they are a riddle, an enigma, a mystery, and a conundrum whose meaning is best arrived at by analyzing the internal construction and selecting which of a number of possible meanings of key words agrees best with the known facts. A scarcity of facts is the ever-present obstacle to understanding. At one time the scriptures were interpreted as supporting or even proving the concept of a flat earth. This erroneous belief, which held the status of an obvious fact, has been supplanted by the positive knowledge that the earth is round. The scriptures were not wrong, they were seriously misinterpreted. Those in authority who had insisted on their misinterpretations brought discredit to themselves and seriously weakened the influence of organized religion. Ever since Galileo religion has been on the defensive against science. The clear lessons of this episode are that it is unsafe to insist on one interpretation to the exclusion of all others and that the possibility of being wrong should always be taken into account.

What if the facts seem insufficient or circumstantial evidences is all there is to go by? This is the common everyday problem of science and one the scientific method is supposed to solve. The unbiased searcher picks his best inferences or, as the legal profession must frequently do, relies on the best evidence the case allows. This is what I have done—the results seem worth reporting. Hopefully, the evidence of succeeding pages will be given a fair trial.

COMMENTS AND REFERENCES

Efforts to prove or disprove the creation scriptures have occupied innumerable minds over the centuries. Because these scriptures deal with very specific natural events most investigators have sought for proof or disproof in the natural sciences which deal with the past. The history of earlier searches is traced in such books as J. C. Greene, 1959, *The Death of Adam,* Mentor Books; Stephen Toulmin and Jane Goodfield, 1961, *The Fabric of the Heavens,* Harper; G. C. Gillispie, 1959, *Genesis and Geology,* Harper; and Arthur Koestler, 1959, *The Sleepwalkers,* Grosset and Dunlap.

In spite of the general failure of science to vindicate the creation scriptures the effort to do so goes on. Some believe that science needs to be reinterpreted within strict scriptural guidelines. Books such as *Up with Creation; Evolution: the Fossils Say No!; Science and Scripture vs. Evolution; Bible Chronology and the Age of the World* have been recently published. Persons interested in these writings and this approach should contact the Institute for Creation Research, 2716 Madison Ave., San Diego, California. By contrast, another class of writing reflects a desire on the part of scientists to reconcile their findings with Genesis by less strict and literal interpretations of its passages. In this category are: Enrico Cantore, 1977, *Scientific Man*, ISH Publications; and Wolfgang Yourgran and A. D. Breck, eds., 1977, *Cosmology, History, and Theology*, a symposium published by Plenum Press.

Numerous theologians, including deep students of the Bible, have come out in favor of reconciliation with science by moderating strict scriptural interpretations. Examples are: Langdon Gilkey, 1965, *Maker of Heaven and Earth*, Anchor Books; Ernst Benz, 1966, *Evolution and Christian Hope*, Doubleday; Alan Richardson, 1961, *The Bible in the Age of Science*, SMC Press, Ltd. (London); and Raymond J. Nogar, 1961, *The Wisdom of Evolution*, New American Library.

It is well to prove all things but it is obvious that lifetimes could be spent studying diverse and contradictory opinions. What is needed are unifying concepts: more synthesis, less analysis.

3

IN THE BEGINNING . . .

In the *beginning* God created the heaven and the earth.

Genesis 1:1

Infinity and eternity are difficult if not impossible for the human mind to comprehend. It is much easier to deal with beginnings and endings because these are what we experience and observe every day. The world is one of finite things with edges, boundaries, dimensions, origins, endings, startings, stoppings, appearances and disappearances. Only when we gaze into the starry heavens do we begin to grasp, however dimly, the idea of infinity. But the same questions that stirred the first inquiring minds thousands of years ago still plague the sophisticated far-seeing scientist of today: What lies beyond? Always one can imagine a boundary but never a boundary with nothing beyond.

The mind dwells more comfortably with the idea of a beginning than it does with no beginning. Two popular theories of the universe may illustrate this. The steady-state theory is that there was no beginning and will be no ending to the universe and the processes within it. What we observe today is a typical example of what could have been seen in the infinite past or might yet be seen at any stage in the infinite future. Stars are observed in process of birth and in every stage leading to their decay and death.

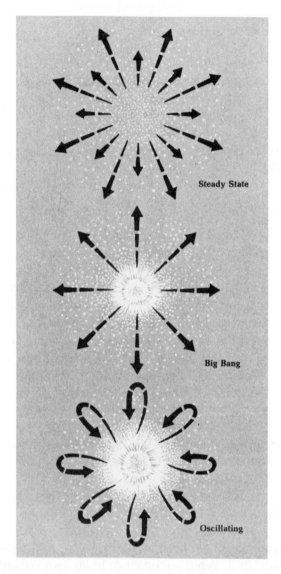

Fig. 3-1 Diagrammatic representations of the three major theories of the universe. Above: steady-state, the universe is expanding but no initial event is postulated; center: the big bang, matter and energy are travelling outward after an initial explosive event; lower: oscillation or pulsation, matter will return to a centralized point to repeat another big-bang event. From Wm. Lee Stokes, *Essentials of Earth History*, 3rd ed. (Englewood Cliffs, N.J.: Prentice-Hall, Inc., 1973), p. 152.

On the other hand is the big-bang theory—the very name is descriptive of an initiating event. At the time of the so-called big-bang, according to the theory, everything was concentrated in one region of space in the form of a compact mass or "super atom." So great is the compactibility of matter that it is calculated that all the constituents of the known universe could be contained in a sphere no larger than that circumscribed by the solar system. At an instant of maximum compression this initial mass exploded with unimaginable violence sending matter and energy speeding outward in all directions to initiate a chain of events which is still in process.

The expansion of the universe is a matter of observation; in fact, it constitutes the strongest evidence for the big-bang theory. All other theories have had to adjust to it in one way or another. The steady-state theory admits that the galaxies are flying apart and concedes that if this has been going on indefinitely they should be at infinite distances from each other. To overcome this difficulty it is proposed that matter from which new galaxies form appears in the spaces between the older ones. According to some, this new matter appears literally out of nothing. Perhaps this belief traces in part to the declaration in the Vulgate version of the Bible, so-called from its common use in the Catholic Church, that God created the world out of nothing (2 Maccabees 7:28). Many believe that new elements are reconstructed from the matter-energy poured into space by older suns and galaxies. Even within the framework of a no-beginning, no-ending universe there must be provisions for the undeniable beginnings and endings that are part of it.

A third concept that to some extent shields the mind from the awful concepts of sameness and endlessness is the oscillation theory. This admits all the facts of an expanding universe and the evidences for a big-bang beginning but envisions a time when expansion will be neutralized and the present universe will begin to contract. Ultimately another primeval atom will appear from which a new universe may emerge. This does not really settle the problems of eternity and infinity, it merely supplies punctuation marks, interruptions, or changes of scene that make eternity less monotonous.

Fig. 3-2 God creating as portrayed in a mural painting by Raffaello Santi, sixteenth century artist. Dynamic interpretations such as this appeal to those who imagine God actively shaping and organizing the materials available to him. As illustrated by this and other drawings and paintings reproduced throughout this book God was perceived in ancient and medieval times in concrete anthromorphic terms. Just how artists and those who commissioned and viewed their works actually thought the creation took place is problematical. Possibly, when the works of creation took in less space and time than they seem to today it was possible to visualize God as actively manipulating the material world. Also, belief in magic was a powerful force in the ancient world and most persons firmly believed that God simply willed or commanded things to appear according to his word. In any event, representations such as the one figured above must have been accepted literally or in an allegorical sense.

With the passage of time the idea of an anthropomorphic God has faded; magic is only an entertaining diversion and solid scientific explanations have been proposed for almost everything. God and his creations can no longer be portrayed in the charming humanized way they once were. Beautiful realistic or romanticized illustrations of all sorts of natural objects from galaxies to atoms may appear in religious art but God has literally disappeared from the picture. Those who view not only these artistic representations but also nature itself must, for the time being, generate their personal inner images of the creator-god in action.

CHAPTER

4

...THE HEAVEN AND THE EARTH...

In the beginning God created *the heaven and the earth.*

Genesis 1:1

Basic to the first verse of Genesis is the assurance that God is the Creator. Furthermore, this verse leaves no doubt as to the comprehensive scope of his works—the heaven and the earth were brought into being. If no other scriptures are considered, the meaning of this statement would seem to be clear and simple —the first things to be produced were the planet and its surroundings without limit and without restriction. However, serious study of the next few passages of Genesis reveals what appears to be alternate meanings of the words *heaven* and *earth.*

The word *earth* has two chief meanings of about equal status and importance in current and probably ancient usage. In the first place, earth designates the loose material making up the surface of the landscape. In this sense it is approximately the same as soil or ground. The second usage designates the specific planet on which we live. In this usage the word is frequently but not always capitalized.

The word earth is also used to distinguish areas of dry land from sea or air. In most instances it is of no great importance to make a distinction and if a distinction is intended the context in which the word is used makes clear which of several meanings

Fig. 4-1 God creating the universe as depicted by the English mystic, poet, and artist, William Blake. Of the many symbolic representations of creation this one is probably the most popular.

applies. The real test of whether or not one meaning is more important than another is what the user intends. Of course, communication has failed if a speaker or writer intends one meaning and his hearers or readers receive another.

This brings us to the question of which meaning applies to the word earth as it appears in this and other creation scriptures. Consider again the first verse of Genesis: "In the beginning God created the heaven and the earth." Does the earth referred to here mean the planet as such or does it designate soil or ground or even perhaps solid matter generally?

The second verse of Genesis would seem to furnish a significant clue. Here we are told that the earth was originally formless and void. It is easier to conceive of elemental matter as existing in a formless condition than it is to think of the planet earth as being formless. It is a central fact of geography and astronomy that the Earth has a very definite nearly spherical shape, this is what makes it a globe and a planet. In a "formless" condition it would not be Earth. From this it seems permissible to assume that the earth of Genesis 1 is solid matter in unorganized condition.

Consider now the term *heaven* which is used in the same sentence as a companion term to *earth*: "In the beginning God created the *heaven and the earth*." Just as there are two common meanings for earth so are there two for heaven: first it is the space of expanse that extends indefinitely above the Earth; second, it is the dwelling place of God. The first meaning is not very precise or specific chiefly because there are usually no limits designated. In some usages heaven seems to designate all of space (the starry heavens); in other places the term seems to refer to the space around our particular Earth.

The second usage of the word heaven designates the place where God resides. Rightly or wrongly this brings to mind a specific locality. In the thinking of the ancients the location of God's abode appears not to have been known except that it is above the earth. For a flat earth this is an understandable concept; it is not very satisfactory for a round one.

With the well-supported assumption that two meanings for the word heaven are admissible it is well to take another look at all of the creation scriptures. In the first verse of Genesis "heaven and earth" are companion or parallel terms. What usage of the word heaven is intended? If we had no more than the first verse we might not be able to tell, but what follows in verses 6 to 8 would seem to leave no doubt: "Let there be a firmament in the midst of the waters, and let it divide the waters from the waters . . . and God called the firmament Heaven. . . ." (Note that here in verse 8 the word heaven is capitalized.) If the literal specific Heaven here described as a product of the second day is God's abode then the heaven of the first day is merely unoccupied space awaiting further organization.

COMMENTS AND REFERENCES

The central problem of this chapter is one of word meanings or semantics. The scriptural text presents us with two words—heaven and earth—both of which have numerous meanings. *The Shorter Oxford English Dictionary* which defines terms chiefly on historical principles gives 10 definitions of the word *heaven* and 17 of the word *earth*. Science cannot tell us which of these definitions is intended in the creation scripture. However, careful attention to the sequence of creative events strongly suggests that the heaven of Genesis 1 must be the entirety of space or at least that part of space associated with God's creative works; earth, in the same vein, must be the material of which things generally are composed. In other words, both terms are to be understood in their most general senses and not in the limited specific senses that are implied in later verses of the same chapter. These general meanings do not conflict with precise grammatical usage or scientific concepts.

Apparently the choice of meanings is left to the judgment of the student. A good comprehensive dictionary and Bible concordance are helpful. Since the interpretations suggested in this chapter are entirely consistent with modern scientific theories of creation they will be put to the test in what follows.

... EARTH ... WITHOUT FORM AND VOID ...

And the earth was without form and void; and
darkness was upon the face of the deep.

Genesis 1:2

The second verse of Genesis 1 refers to conditions immediately following the creation of matter and space. The cryptic words *void* and *without form* are employed to describe the rudimentary state of organization at this time. Those who would put the account in familiar modern language might say things were chaotic. The word chaos is from a Greek word meaning empty space. But the idea that nothing existed at this time is contrary to actuality—earth was there. But chaos has also been defined as a mixed mass without form or order; in some usages there is a suggestion that the disorder of chaos has arisen from a previous state of order or that the disorder is temporary, pending attention and organization.

Void is a curious term with a number of meanings. It may designate that which is empty, vacant or not occupied; the emptiness it describes may be due to the lack of inhabitants or possessors. Void may signify the condition of being without something specific such as life or meaning. Also it may mean not productive of any effect or being in vain. These meanings are all in a different vein from the legal definition which means not binding, null or without effect. Empty is a synonym of void with many of the same meanings such as containing nothing, being destitute, not supplied, unfruitful, vacated, meaningless, and unoccupied.

The earth or earth material is also described as being without form. The improbability of a formless planet has already been discussed and the conclusion reached that the earth referred to in these introductory verses is unorganized matter in general and not the planet Earth. To refer to a planet as being without form is self-contradictory. It is the fact that Earth has a form which makes it a planet and not a shapeless mass. A planet might be void but not formless. However, an unorganized mass of matter can be both formless and void at the same time. Such distinctions are helpful in choosing between the two definitions of earth that are permissible at this point.

COMMENTS AND REFERENCES

A basic belief of scientists who deal with matter is that it is composed basically of a relatively few fundamental or elemental units. Physicists are devising expensive and complex equipment and experiments to take matter apart and put it back together in order to learn more about the so-called subatomic particles. The electron and proton, formerly thought to be indivisible and irreducible, have been divided and reduced and the end may not yet be in sight.

No one doubts that the elemental units of matter-energy began to be assembled at the beginning of the universe. A very satisfying aspect of the big-bang theory is that it makes provision for the creation of the first atoms of hydrogen, simplest of the chemical elements, on a massive scale within the first few minutes of time. Following this for millions of years there was little more than hydrogen in the universe. The assembly of heavier, more complex elements had to await the appearance of the dense aggregations known as galaxies. The interval of quiescence, with hydrogen atoms dispersing outward in utter darkness is perfectly described by the phrase "without form and void."

Any good physics text has chapters on the structure of matter and its relation to energy but the subject is moving ahead so rapidly that text-book writers cannot keep up with the latest discoveries. The cosmic beginnings as visualized by astronomers are described in many books: two are Steven Weinberg, 1977, *The First Three Minutes: A Modern View of the Origin of the Universe*, Basic Books; and George Gamow, 1956, *The Creation of the Universe*, Viking Press. Gamow is credited with developing the big-bang theory to its present level of high credibility.

... DARKNESS ... UPON THE FACE OF THE DEEP ...

"And the earth was without form, and void;
and darkness was upon the face of the deep. . . ."
                                          Genesis 1:2

The conditions described in the second verse of Genesis 1 were essential steps in the development of elemental matter from an unorganized state to a sphere suitable for human life. The earth referred to is not the finished planet, rather universal unorganized matter, primitive, basic, and elemental—but with endless potential for future development. This concept of an alternate meaning of earth opens up possibilities of understanding that are otherwise impossible. Consider the state of darkness as a step in the process of creation rather than a condition that prevailed before creation began.

In human experience darkness is the opposite of light. Darkness is not usually thought of as being created—it is the inevitable state of things when and where there is no light. One does not usually think of darkness being created to overcome light but rather light being created to dispel darkness. It is only natural to regard darkness as the original primeval state of things and to believe that the entire universe was in a state of previously unbroken darkness before God commenced his work. Scriptures leave open the possibility that the darkness was temporary and

pertained only to the system from which the earth would ultimately emerge. Furthermore, looking at the matter from a scientific viewpoint, darkness is an essential step in the early history
of the universe. The command: let there be light may have been
preceded by one even more necessary and just as fundamental:
let there be darkness!

These thoughts are not totally beyond experience. Every
plant needs light to grow and develop and yet it cannot begin to
grow in the presence of light. Only in the darkness of the soil will
a plant germinate and only in the still darker interior of the seed
will the embryo begin to swell. Every seed in effect must be taken
out of light and placed in darkness before it can fill the really
important part of its existence. The egg is a symbolic object to the

Fig. 6-1   Many objects seen in space have a cloud-like or nebulous appearance. Some are light, others are dark; some have hazy ill-defined boundaries,
others have sharp edges or "faces". This example, the Horsehead Nebula,
gives a mental impression of the darkness that may have prevailed upon "the
face of the deep" as described in Genesis 1:2.

mystical mind and an unsurpassed example of evolutionary adaptation to the scientist. Within its dark interior occurs one of natures most amazing transformations and nothing is more dramatic than the hatching process when a new being emerges into the light to begin a totally new phase of existence.

And so with ourselves. It is in the darkness of our mother's body that we begin life—in the darkness of the womb we grow until we are ready to come forth. The ancient phrase "seeing the light of day" is almost synonymous with being born.

That there must be an interval of darkness in the creation of the universe is an essential requirement of the big-bang theory. This stage occurs between the production of the chemical elements in the big bang and their condensation into light-generating galaxies. Darkness took over when the powerful radiant energy of the initial explosion had faded and was no longer strong enough to prevent gravity from asserting its influence. Gravity is a weak force among smaller entities of matter but a strong and dominating one when the entirety of the universe is considered. Slowly and in total darkness the widely dispersed atoms of elemental hydrogen and helium were drawn into immense formless clouds. Centers of gravity with maximum density of matter were established in each such cloud and the stage was set for more spectacular developments. Slowly, as atoms and molecules drew closer together, they collided more frequently causing a steady rise in temperature. Eventually at temperatures of several hundred degrees light was generated and the period of darkness came to an end.

Another thought emerges from the terminology of the text. The phrase "face of the deep" is there for a purpose. No matter how the term face is used it calls to mind something solid, or at least something with a form behind the face. Thus we refer to the face of the land, or the face of the Sun or of the Moon; and, of course, a human face implies a head and body. Perhaps the reference, face of the deep, is to signify that there was a mass, at least a separate entity, with a surface or discontinuity surrounding the material which God intended to organize. A dense cloud has a face just as surely as does a solid body such as the earth or moon. It is now an astronomical truism that stars are born from dark clouds and the first stars probably appeared in a cloud of elemental matter.

Scientists are fond of using the word interface and experts in many fields know well enough that it is at the interface of things that most physical and chemical actions take place. Erosion and weathering take place at the interface of land and atmosphere or between land and water. Evaporation is a phenomenon of the interface of water and atmosphere. Exchange of heat and cold goes forward across interfaces, ice melts and water freezes at an interface. And chemical reactions, ever rapid explosions, progress along a face or front. Life itself, most complex expression of natural processes, operates by reactions at interfaces provided by cell walls and interior membranes. An interface implies heterogeneity and heterogeneity is prerequisite to reaction. Not much, if anything can go on in a homogeneous

Fig. 6-2   An immense black cloud appears to be streaming from a great star in the constellation Monoceros.

(Courtesy Palomar Observatory, California Institute of Technology.)

state. The expression "face of the deep" implies the possibility of action and reaction yet to come.

COMMENTS AND REFERENCES

Of all inclusive theories in science none can be said to have withstood the tests of vigorous examination better than the big-bang theory. It is complex in detail but simple enough to be readily explainable and comprehensible on a popular level. Many good books and articles are available: George Gamow, 1956, *The Creation of the Universe*, Viking Press; Isaac Asimov, 1966, *The Universe*, Discus Books; James A. Coleman, 1963, *Modern Theories of the Universe*, The New American Library; Steven Weinberg, 1977, *The First Three Minutes: A Modern View of the Universe*, Basic Books. George Gamow is credited with establishing the big-bang theory on a firm theoretical footing; Isaac Asimov is a foremost popularizer of scientific subjects; James Coleman's book is notable for a simplified but comprehensive and unbiased presentation of competing theories; Steven Weinberg gives an updated account that integrates new findings and thinking about the first few minutes of creation.

... THE SPIRIT OF GOD MOVED UPON THE FACE OF THE WATERS.

And the Spirit of God moved upon the face of the waters.

Genesis 1:2

The first sentence of the creation scriptures names two created things, namely, heaven and earth. For each of these more than one definition is possible. Earth may be the planet of man's habitation or it may be solid matter generally; heaven may be the specific place where God resides or it may be space generally. What follows after the first verses strongly suggests that the broader more general meanings of both terms are intended. The first act of creation was to produce space and visible matter and not the planet Earth and nearby space.

The second sentence of the creation scripture introduces another term for which there is only one definition and this presents difficulties. The term is *water*. What is to be understood by the term "face of the waters" that occur in the scriptures? There is ample reason or excuse for the traditional view that the water or waters referred to must be the only deep water we know much about, namely, that contained in the oceans of the earth. But this cannot be if the earth of the preceding verse (Genesis 1:1) is not the planet Earth. It is as simple as this: no planet, no oceans. And while we are thinking about possible meanings, why is the term "face of the deep" used in the preceding sentence as if there were two faces or materials or conditions to be seriously considered?

Significant answers emerge when earth-centered interpretations of things are replaced with space-oriented ones. Brief mention must be made of what has been discovered in extraterrestrial environments. In addition to solid bodies of various kinds the galaxy contains much gas and dust referred to as interstellar matter or the interstellar medium. This consists of matter left over from star formation and also of matter expelled from former stars as they exploded or disintegrated. Generally interstellar matter is so thinly dispersed that there is only one atom or molecule per cubic centimeter or so but there are local aggrega-

Fig. 7-1 The relatively small dark objects called globules are non-luminous clouds of dust and gas thought to be forerunners of stars or groups of stars. Many have been found to be rich in water and similar substances. The sharp outline and contrast between light and darkness is an example of an interface. Perhaps a distinction is to be made between the "face of the deep" and "face of the waters" of Genesis 1:2. This example is the Rosette Nebula.
(Courtesy Palomar Observatory, California Institute of Technology.)

tions which may be spoken of literally as dense clouds. Interstellar clouds are transparent to varying degrees; some are so dense that they appear as vast, utterly dark patches; others are self-luminous, while still others appear to shine because there are suns burning deep within them.

Study of interstellar material is advancing rapidly chiefly because of recent developments in radio astronomy. By study of microwave measurement the elements and molecules present in space can be identified even though they give off no visible radiation. Results have been surprising; the number of known interstellar molecules is 50 at the time of this writing and the list will certainly grow with time.

Among the molecules so far identified are the cyanogen radical, CN; hydroxyl radical, OH; ammonia, NH_3; water, H_2O; formaldehyde, $H_2C = O$; Carbon monoxide, CO; hydrogen, H_2; hydrogen cyanide, HCN; cyanoacetylene, $HC = C\text{-}CN$; methyl alcohol, CH_3OH; formic acid, $HCOOH$; carbon monosulfide, CS; formamide, $HC (NH_2)O$; silicon monoxide, SiO; carbonyl sulfide, OCS; acetonitrile, $CH_3C = CH$; acetaldehyde, CH_3CHO; thioformaldehyde, $H_2C = S$; hydrogen sulfide, H_2S; and methyleneimine, $H_2C = NH$. In late 1976 acetylene, C_2H_2 was discovered by infrared radiation. Infrared emissions can be detected in broad daylight and probably many new molecules will be found by this means. Some astronomers are convinced that almost any complex molecule can exist in space. We are finding only those which can make their presence known over great distances.

The study of the chemistry of interstellar material is clearly just beginning but what has already been discovered is very significant in any thinking about the origin of the earth. Even before the identification of specific elements and compounds in the clouds of space it was fairly well established that these clouds are the raw material out of which stars are formed. Now that some of the constituents of these clouds have been identified we know at least some of the potential building blocks of the earth and its neighbors. We say *some* of the blocks because there are many elements and even more compounds that cannot make their presence known to earth-bound observers. This is especially true of dust as compared to gas. Dust particles may have almost any composition and may be crystalline or non-crystalline, magnetic or non-magnetic, and of course have a wide range of possible reactions to radiation.

The present discussion may be restricted to water (H_2O) and to the hydroxyl component (OH) with which it is commonly associated. The hydroxyl radical was discovered in space in 1963, and water in 1969. Ammonia (NH_3) was identified in 1968. The presence of water and ammonia is not surprising since hydrogen is the most common element in the universe and the reactive elements oxygen and nitrogen are also abundant. Both water and ammonia solidify at relatively high temperatures, astronomically speaking, and it is supposed on indirect evidence

Fig. 7-2   A lighted nebula in the constellation Gemini. A cloud of luminous gas with a definite front or face is moving through space at high velocity.
(Courtesy Palomar Observatory, California Institute of Technology.)

that much of the dust in certain clouds is in the form of ice. In other areas water must occur as droplets in liquid form; under higher temperatures the gaseous state must prevail.

When I commenced to write this book the amount of information on water in space was so limited my discussion was almost without foundation. Water was discovered in space in 1969; advances since then have been almost unbelievable. It is gratifying that discoveries are favorable to my ideas.

Fig. 7-3 The Trifid Nebula in the constellation Sagittarius. Many faces between dark and light masses and between patches of different luminosity (left margin) are visible.

(Courtesy Palomar Observatory, California Institute of Technology.)

Water makes itself known to astronomers chiefly because it can be stimulated under certain conditions to radiate energy in wave-lengths beyond or longer than those visible to the eye as light. It is not a simple matter — the water molecule H_2O radiates only because it can operate as a maser (microwave amplification by stimulated emission of radiation). A maser operates when molecules, such as water, absorb energy from infrared (heat) sources and re-radiate the extra energy thus acquired in radio waves. It is a process of amplification or, as it is commonly called a pumping action. The maser reaction operates only when special conditions prevail. Temperature limits which favor the process are in the range 20 to 1000 K and the concentration of molecules is relatively low.

As it turns out the conditions under which water vapor can act as a maser are those associated with early (cooler) stages of star formation. The entire subject is relatively new. The association of H_2O masers and OH (hydroxyl) masers with early stages of star formation was not appreciated until the mid 70's. It is most exciting to know that elements and even compounds such as water can now be positively identified in space. Great new instruments such as radio telescopes and interferometers are being constructed with the potential of gathering as much information in the future as that gained in the past by the optical telescope. What can be said at this time merely introduces a subject destined to grow rapidly in importance in the years ahead.

The connection with creation scriptures is this: water exists in the clouds of space and is known to be abundant in areas where new stars are forming. Reasoning and speculating from these facts it may be assumed for the sake of continuing the story that water may be essential to the formation of solar systems like the one to which the Earth belongs. In any event the earth is well supplied with water and must have emerged from a water-rich environment. Of course, it is realized that the original cloud contained many other substances besides water, some perhaps in amounts greater than water. But the original mix, no matter what the composition, could well be called water or at least water-like in physical and chemical properties. As described in the previous chapter the waters had a "face," implying their existence in a body separated from space or from material of another sort. This description agrees with what astronomers regard as a protocloud from which a sun-planet system might emerge.

COMMENTS AND REFERENCES

Water (liquid, gas, or solid H_2O) has recently been discovered in space and may, in fact, be a major component of many great cloud-like aggregations. Several books that treat the subject are: Neale Watson, 1973, *The Dusty Universe*, Academic Publications; Beverly L. Lynds, 1976, *Dark Nebulae, Globules, and Protostars*, University of Arizona Press; T. De Jong and A. Maeder (eds.), 1977, *Star Formation*, International Astronomical Union Symposium No. 75, D. Reidel Publishing Company; Cyril Ponnamperuma (ed.), 1976, *Chemical Evolution of the Giant Planets*, Academic Press.

Representative papers ranging from popular to technical include: Dale F. Dickinson, 1978, Cosmic masers, *Scientific American*, vol. 238; George H. Herbig, 1974, Interstellar smog, *American Scientist*, vol. 62, no. 2; H. C. van de Hulst, 1953, "Empty" space, *Scientific American*, vol. 188, no. 6; K. J. Johnson, S. K. Knowles, and P. R. Schwartz, 1972, Microwave celestial water-vapor sources, *Sky and Telescope*, vol. 44, no. 2. A recent statement on the subject is R. Genzel and D. Downes, 1977, H_2O in the galaxy; sites of newly formed stars: *Astronomy and Astrophysics* Supplemental Series, *A European Journal*, vol. 30, p. 145-168. This last-named article describes 82 water vapor sources of which 32 are new discoveries. This research should eliminate any doubt as to the close relationship of water vapor and star formation.

...LET THERE BE LIGHT...

> And God said, Let there be light: and there was
> light.
>
> Genesis 1:3

God is often portrayed as being surrounded by light. At his transfiguration it is declared that the face of Christ "did shine as the sun, and his raiment was white as the light." Moses encountered God in the bush that "burned with fire, and the bush was not consumed."

Since God is a personage of light, it is inconceivable that he could exist in darkness. As the Creator he may have brought forth light on many occasions before the event recorded in the third verse of the first chapter of Genesis. What then is to be understood by that profound utterance: Let there be light?

It cannot be without significance that darkness is mentioned before light in the creation scriptures. Light and darkness are opposites and antagonists as it were; when one prevails the other is absent. The presence of the darkness mentioned in scripture must have been marked by a corresponding absence or withdrawal of light. Is the creation of darkness perhaps more important here than the creation of light? Strangely, scriptures tell nothing about the previous period of light; its radiance was fading when the first creative day began.

There are about 250 references to light in the Bible. As might be expected these references relate to much more than manifestations in the physical sense. Light is often mentioned in connection with that which is spiritual or intellectual. Christ said: "I am the *light* of the world: he that followeth me shall not walk in darkness, but shall have the *light* of life." (John 8:12.) Light at least in scripture obviously has several basic meanings and the relation of physical light to spiritual things is beyond the scope of this discussion. Here we will concentrate on light as science describes it.

What is light? The author of the latest *Encyclopedia Britannica* article on the topic observes that light cannot be defined in terms of anything simpler or more directly appreciated by the senses than itself. Light has also been defined as a form of energy conveyed through empty space at high velocities. For practical purposes light is that manifestation of energy visible to the eye. According to another definition light is a form of electromagnetic radiation with wavelengths between about 310 and 1,050 millimicrons (from 16 to 30 millionths of an inch). Another definition is that it is energy contained in small packets called photons, a photon being regarded as a special type of fundamental particle.

Fig. 8-1　Light flooding the dark and lifeless earth as depicted by the nineteenth century artist John Martin.

44

These definitions introduce one of the great puzzles of science. Should light be considered as a wave or as a particle? In the early 19th century when many experiments were being performed with light the wave theory held sway. Properties such as reflection, refraction and interference that are demonstrated routinely to all physics students are best explained as wave phenomena and can be duplicated by ordinary ripples in standing water. That light travels at the high velocity of 186,000 miles per second was demonstrated in 1927 but this did not settle the matter of whether it is a wave or a particle.

With the advent of atomic physics attention shifted to the problem of how light is created and destroyed or absorbed. Here the evidence favors the particle theory. The fact that there is a lower limit to the energy carried by light (3.5×10^{-12} erg or 3.5×10^{-19} joule) and that it is in this or multiples of it that all light can be described gave rise to the necessity of dealing with it in terms of what are called photons. The concept that light must be regarded as an assemblage of entities was established by Albert Einstein in 1905. Later in the period of 1925-1930 the field of quantum mechanics appeared and has yielded a more unified view of what light is. In quantum mechanics light is not regarded strictly as a particle or a wave; the two are treated as compatible. The problem is when to regard light as a wave and when to regard it as a particle.

Unsolved as yet is whether the photon has weight or mass. It is the nature of light that it must be always in motion. Whatever it is that emerges as light is not light before it emerges; likewise, after it is absorbed it is no longer light. This is a most critical point. Light can transmit information and energy across vast distances but can it transmit matter as well? It has not been proven that the mass of a photon is absolutely zero; if it does have mass it must be exceedingly small. But if even the most minute quantity of matter is transmitted by light, the overall long-term effects are of great importance in the evolution of the universe.

Light is generated by atoms and molecules of many kinds when they are subject to outside influences such as application of heat, mutual crowding and the impact of radiation or other

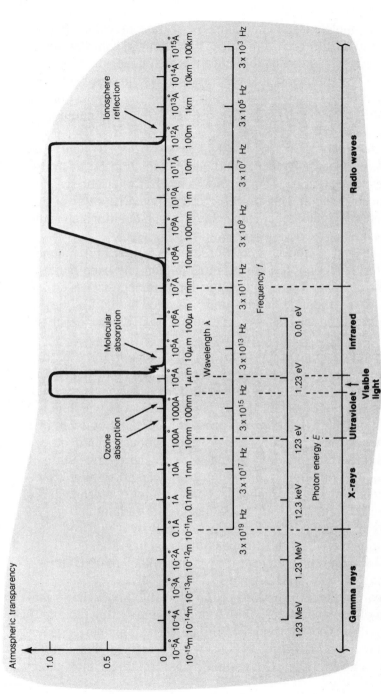

Fig. 8-2   Diagram showing the classification of light and other radiation according to wave length. Names along the lower line designate broad classes of radiation; the upper line shows the entire spectrum in terms of angstrom units. This can be translated in terms of the shortest wave-lengths on the left to the longest wave-lengths on the right. The two elevated peaks on this line represent the radiation that penetrates the earth's atmosphere.
(Courtesy NASA.)

atoms and molecules. Light comes in different colors (wavelengths) and at different intensities. Variations in light are determined by the structure of the matter which generates it. Since the most abundant element is hydrogen this is the source of most of the light of the universe. Even though it is the simplest of the elements hydrogen can still give rise to light at a number of energy levels.

Matter not only generates light, it also absorbs light. The existence of specific elements and compounds that occur in distant stars and galaxies is made known by characteristic ways in which these elements emit or absorb radiation. The study of this phenomenon is spectroscopy, the chief instrument of which is the spectroscope.

What light is and how it is created is a vast and complex subject to which only the barest introduction has been made in these paragraphs. To return to the topic under discussion we should inquire about conditions that prevailed on the first day of creation when under certain circumstances God said: Let there be light.

The appearance of light at a specific stage in the evolution of a typical galaxy such as ours is recognized as a critical event in all modern theories of the universe. This event holds a prominent place in the theory of the expanding universe which is the dominant or ruling theory at the present time. Light appears in a galaxy when an originally diffuse and lightless cloud of gas destined to become a galaxy reaches a sufficiently high state of compaction. As matter is forced into smaller and smaller space the electrons, atoms and molecules at the center of a protogalaxy collide with increasing frequency to generate radiant energy. At first only heat is produced; this is followed by a dull red glow which appears when the temperature reaches about 800° K. Eventually, when the temperature reaches about 10,000,000° K., thermonuclear reactions begin and a star is born.

According to late versions of the big-bang theory the formations of galaxies began less than a million years after the expulsion of matter from the center of the universe. This period is not a long one in the astronomical sense but as described in chapter 11 many important and essential transformations took place during it.

Fig. 8-3 One of the most distant objects yet discovered, this quasar, was detected by the x-ray telescope. Quasars are brilliant and mysterious objects believed to be near the boundaries of the universe. If this is true they were formed early in its history and may be forerunners of the more familiar galaxies. The most distant quasar yet discovered is over fifteen billion light years away, hence over fifteen billion years old. The universe may be somewhat older. Quasars may thus signal the first appearance of light, an event that comes early both in the scriptures and in cosmology.

(Courtesy NASA.)

It was after the lengthy period of universal darkness when the galaxies were in an early stage of condensation that God seems to have entered the scene. His agency in bringing forth light is not described in detail but what is revealed in scripture is thought-provoking. God's words were: Let there be light. The word "let" is a significant clue. Aside from its usual meaning of giving permission let also means to allow or to remove restraints. Moses said to Pharaoh, Let my people go. In other words, remove their restraints or give your permission. God's agency in the production of light was to remove existing restrictions or to bring about conditions such that light might spontaneously appear. Darkness prevailed before God spoke or his spirit moved upon the face of the deep, then light appeared. With the appearance of light a new phase of creation began. Just how the words or actions of God might be explained scientifically is not clear; but it would not seem to be an eternally impenetrable mystery, something that intelligent and righteous minds cannot comprehend. Perhaps no great reorganizations of latent matter and space were required to generate light at this critical stage. If the proper materials are already available, only a spark is needed to start a mighty furnace or ignite an everlasting flame. It was the intelligent application of power and authority at the right place and time that initiated the process of the generation of light as the most important event of the first creative period. The light that was kindled at the center of the galaxy has continued to shine ever since like a great central fire. But other important appearances of light were to follow. Although it is not stated specifically light appeared and alternated with darkness on each of the six creative periods. This alternation is God's way of sub-dividing creation—he called the light Day and the darkness Night. The significance of this subdivision is a major theme of what follows.

COMMENTS AND REFERENCES

Light is a universal phenomenon and the subject of much scientific research. Brief discussions that cover essential aspects of the subject as it is understood today are found in the latest editions of the *Encyclopedia Britannica* (1977) and *Encyclopedia Americana* (1977). All college and high school texts have chapters on light; current approaches are found in Virgilia Acosta, Clyde Harper, and B. J. Graham, 1973, *Essentials of Modern Physics*, Harper and Row; Peter J. Brancazio, 1975, *The Nature of Physics*, Macmillan; George A. Williams, 1969, *Elementary Physics*, McGraw-Hill.

Books dealing specifically with light are: Vasco R. Ronchi, 1962, *The Nature of Light*, Harvard University Press; A. A. Sabra, 1967, *Theories of Light*, Oldbourne; and A. C. S. van Heel and C. H. F. Velzel, 1968, *What Is Licht?* (English translation, *What Is Light?*, 1968).

The production of light as an innate capability of matter is a subject covered in various degrees of technicality in physics textbooks. The best discussion I have found is by Trevor Weeks, Gamma rays and the origin of cosmic radiation, *Astronomy*, June 1977. This explains the origin of radio waves, visible light and infra-red radiation in terms of reactions of matter. The accompanying illustration is excellent.

A readable, well-illustrated book is *Light and Vision*, 1969, Life Science Library, Time, Inc. Other biological aspects of the subject are discussed in Life and Light, by George Wald, *Scientific American*, October 1959.

CHAPTER

9

...GOD DIVIDED THE
LIGHT FROM THE DARKNESS

And God saw the light, that it was good: and
God divided the light from the darkness.

Genesis 1:4

Light is the universal messenger not only from remote places but also from the distant past. The basic yardstick of astronomy, the light-year, is a measure of both time and distance. As telescopes gather light from the far-off reaches of space they are also probing far into the past. With improvements in instruments and techniques astronomers are hoping to reach the edge of the universe. According to their best theories, if they can find this distant boundary they will also be observing the beginning of the universe.

Paradoxically the messages of light cannot be perceived without darkness. It is the interplay of the two which makes meaningful observation possible. The mind can imagine both a universe of light and a universe of darkness. Physicists can describe either of these as verifiable possibilities and can speculate why we live in a universe where both exist in so many interesting and contrasting ways.

We are informed that when God saw or comprehended the light he proceeded to divide or cause it to be divided from the darkness. But we are not told how this was done. To the earthbound observer light is divided from darkness simply by the rising and setting of the sun. In ancient times it was believed the sun did all the moving while the earth stood still in the center of things. Later when the true nature of the solar system became evident it was the rotation of the earth that was seen to divide the light from the darkness. In other words a purely mechanical process did the dividing. And it is this commonplace everyday earth-sun mechanism that probably comes to the mind of most readers when they try to visualize the original division of light from darkness. But that this cannot be the method of the first few divisions of the creative periods is apparent from the scriptures themselves—the sun did not appear until the fourth day.

There are many ways besides the revolution of the earth that light may be divided from darkness and even though the methods may not be positively identified for each of the six successive creative periods there is no lack of interesting and varied possibilities. In the first place light may be divided from darkness

Fig. 9-1 This woodcut, published in 1572 as an illustration for the Old Testament, shows God dividing the light from the darkness.

strictly on the basis of time—one period may be entirely dark and another entirely light: that is, there might be universal darkness followed by universal light.

Possibilities multiply. Light and darkness may be separated merely by the actions of clouds. There may be a dark cloud in a well-lighted sky. This is not confined to earthbound skies. The depths of space contain dark clouds in abundance, some in the most brilliant nebula. Locally, darkness can exist in the midst of light. The opposite can be illustrated in the same way. A beacon may shine in darkness, a ray of sunlight may break through clouds. And in space stars may be seen coming into being from very dark clouds. These are examples of the separation of light and darkness by local conditions.

There is more. Light may succeed darkness or darkness may succeed light in the history of individual astronomical bodies. A dark cloud of matter may be compressed into a blazing star. A star may degenerate into a lightless dwarf. Smaller objects such as planets or satellites may melt and become self-luminous or they may solidify and return to darkness.

Fig. 9-2   God dispelling clouds of darkness from the earth. From an illustrated Luther Bible published in Nürnberg, 1702.

And finally, on a still more restricted scale, part of a single body may undergo a separation of light and darkness by having one side lighted while the other side is in shadow. If it rotates the separation of light and darkness is experienced by all of its surface on a regular basis. That only the last method describes the familiar sequence of earth's days and nights is obvious.

THIS IS THE GENESIS CODE: Each creative "day" consists of a period dominated by darkness and a period dominated by light. Earth emerged from chaos as a product of the progressive succession of six such periods. The creative days were not of equal duration and are not intended to be measures of time. They are not the periods, epochs, and eras invented by geologists. Their meaning is celestial and not terrestrial. They are God's divisions of his own creations. When we fully recognize them for what they are we will comprehend the meaning of the creation scriptures.

COMMENTS AND REFERENCES

The reality of alternating periods of light and darkness during the progressive history of the universe, galaxy, solar system, and earth may be verified by studying up-to-date material on cosmology, astronomy, and geology. References given in connection with other chapters are sufficient. However the successive periods of light and darkness must be carefully noted or it may not be apparent that they actually existed.

For comments by theological writers on the days of creation consult *The Interpreters Bible*, 1952, vol. 1, p. 468-491; *The Universal Jewish Encyclopedia* (1941 edition), vol. 3, p. 395; *The Encyclopedia of Biblical Interpretation* (Jewish), volume on Genesis 1, p. 38-85; and *The New Catholic Encyclopedia*, vol. 4, p. 423-424.

...GOD CALLED THE LIGHT DAY
AND THE DARKNESS...NIGHT

*And God called the light Day, and the darkness
he called Night.*

Genesis 1:5

F ew things in earthly experience exceed in importance the
successive alternations of light and darkness that men call days
and nights. All human activity, individual as well as collective, is
governed by the fact that such alternations occur. Sleep and
wakefulness, activity and inactivity, rest and labor follow the
pattern of day and night. We "count the days" before, between,
and after events that are of importance to us. Other figures of
speech such as our "days being numbered" or "days drawing to
a close" are commonly used.

Early in life we are taught what it is that causes the days
and nights. We learn about the revolution of the earth and its
relation to the central sun. Every school child becomes aware of
that which Copernicus struggled to comprehend and convey to
his contemporaries. The day as we define it is arbitrarily divided
into twenty-four hours and the ability to tell time by the clock is
another vital piece of our youthful education. Small wonder that
such hard-earned knowledge gives every informed person a
rather definite concept of what is meant by the words day and
night.

Common sense and a minimum of research should convince
anyone, however, that God's Days and Nights cannot be the days
and nights of human experience. The scriptural account is clear
on this point. There could be no ordinary astronomical day-night
relationships without a light-giving sun and no sun is mentioned
until the fourth day of creation. It seems to have been the intent
of God to commence the designation of creative days even while
the earth was without form, certainly before the "firmament" of
heaven was created.

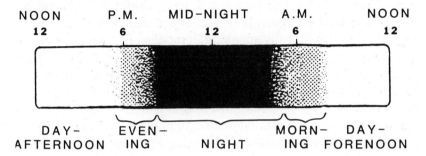

THE ORDINARY 24-HOUR DAY

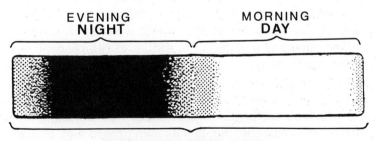

THE CREATIVE DAY

Fig. 10-1 God's day and man's day compared. The ordinary 24-hour day,
diagrammed at the top of the illustration, has become so strongly established in
man's time keeping scheme that we may forget that there are other possible
divisions and meanings. God's creative day, as declared in Genesis 1:5 consists of a period of darkness and a period of light. The darkness corresponds to
the evening of the Jewish Sabbath and the light corresponds to its morning.

These obvious scriptural facts should serve as a caution that the creative days were different from man's days. The scriptures leave no doubt as to the intended meaning—light is called Day, darkness is called Night. Only this and nothing more; no earth-sun relationships are described or required at this stage.

As the story unfolds this conclusion is verified: a succession of distinct "days" is described, each with its particular events and products. That such division is more than a mere literary device or arbitrary convenience becomes evident when the facts and well-founded theories of astronomy are considered. This will be treated more fully in appropriate chapters that follow.

Strictly and literally speaking in modern English an evening and a morning do not make a day; they are the transitions from day to night and night to day respectively. Neither does the interval from evening to morning constitute the day; it is only half of a day in terms of elapsed time, and in general experience it is the dark part of the day and would commonly be called night.

There are good reasons to believe that the definition of a scriptural day of creation is not the same as that which prevails today. According to long-established usage—perhaps beginning initially with the making of reliable clocks—the day by modern definition commences at midnight and ends at midnight. The transition, from one day to the next taking place as it does while most people are sleeping, causes a minimum of confusion. The common designation AM (for ante-meridian and PM (for post-meridian) tells us which side of midnight we are referring to. But every time zone has a different meridian of reference; this is so that the steady progression of light and darkness around the earth can be divided into 24 arbitrary steps that are more convenient for human use. There is however one master meridian to which all earthly time is referred. This meridian, passing through Greenwich, England, has its own progression of time like every other possible point; but by common consent the time at this place becomes everyone's time—namely Greenwich time. Everyone who uses this standard knows what time it really is in one simple reference, he need not have a wall full of clocks.

The biblical day was established before clocks were invented and meridians established. It is based on the natural reoccurrence of light and darkness. The tradition of the Jewish religion preserves this ancient meaning. According to the *Encyclopedia Judaica*: "Sabbath and festivals begin in the evening and terminate at the start of the following night." This is also honored in the halakic postulate that "the day goes after the night." God has employed this analogy throughout the creation scripture in describing the succession of events which are called nights and days.

Putting this interpretation to the test we must conclude that the first creative day began while there was yet light but darkness was approaching. The ensuing darkness was the night of the first creative period. Then followed a period of light that concluded it. Under this interpretation we reach the somewhat surprising conclusion that the creation of heaven and earth mentioned in the first verse of Genesis should probably not be included in the six creative periods.

This agrees with what has been said in chapter 8 on the topic of the appearance of darkness early in the creative accounts. In summary, the first day of creation, as God evidently intended the expression to be understood, began, not with the "big bang" of science but sometime after as its effects were dimming and a period of darkness was approaching. This is not to be interpreted that God had nothing to do with things before the six days of creation began. He created the heaven and the earth of Genesis 1:1 just as surely as he created anything else. One conclusion is that there was a long period of inaction, perhaps one might call it chaotic or disorganized, in the universe of space and matter, before God selected a part of it from which to construct an earth.

COMMENTS AND REFERENCES

God's decision to call the light Day and the darkness Night as a method of timekeeping throughout the creation is not a matter needing scientific verification. A little thought and research will convince anyone that the relation of light and darkness to what we now call day and night is not the only possible arrangement. The people of the Old Testament had a different scheme, one that is still observed in the Jewish festivals and Sabbath observance. Comments on this ancient timekeeping method are found in *The Universal Jewish Encyclopedia* (1941 edition), p. 493; *The Interpreters Bible* (1952), vol. 1, p. 470-471; and *The Catholic Dictionary of Theology* (1976), p. 138.

...EVENING AND MORNING
...FIRST DAY

And the evening and the morning were the first
day.

Genesis 1:5

Long before telescopes were invented the heavens were seen
to be populated by many stationary lights and a scattered few
that move. These became known as fixed stars and planets
(wanderers). With time, as the true scale of things unfolded, the
earth was recognized as a planet and the sun as a star. Still
later, as instruments improved, another class of objects, the
galaxies, was discovered. Galaxies are groups of multitudes of
stars. The discovery of these aggregations and the proof that our
solar system is a minor component of one of them ranks as a most
significant discovery of modern astronomy.

Galaxies have been classified according to shape as spiral,
elliptical, and irregular. The majority of galaxies are classed as
spirals and the home of the solar system, the Milky Way galaxy,
is of this type. Any discussion of the ultimate origin of the planet
Earth must take into account the problem of how spiral aggregations may have originated. At present there are more
questions than answers. According to one authority, reporting on
a 1979 symposium, two of the three unsolved problems of cosmology (study of the structure of the universe) are the origin of

the density fluctuations that gave rise to galaxies in the early universe and the subsequent evolution of their morphology and general characteristics.

What went on between the Big Bang and the formation of galaxies has been satisfactorily explained in terms of the expansion of the universe. For literally a split second when expansion commenced matter was in its most elemental, unorganized condition and the temperature was on the order of trillions of degrees. The universe was filled with gamma rays, technically defined as electromagnetic radiation with the highest possible frequency. They may also be conceived as extremely energetic particles or protons. In one second temperatures had fallen to billions of degrees and heavier particles such as protons and neutrons were forming. It may not be incorrect to say that the chief activity of the first second of time was the conversion of energy into matter. Put in another way radiation condensed into particles.

For a period measured in thousands of years radiation dominated matter. A comparison has been made with logs, representing matter, in a river of water, representing energy. If there are few logs and a violent flood the logs are tossed about and are carried along without resistance. If, on the other hand, there are many logs and little water the logs are dominant and will control the flow patterns of the stream. Decreasing density of available matter inhibited the formation of all but the simplest of elements, hydrogen and helium. During a period of a few thousand years, virtually the entire available store of matter went into the formation of these two elements and radiation sank to negligible levels.

As light faded the universe entered a phase that is well described by the biblical phrase "dark and void." This phase lasted for a few million years and might have gone on forever had not another factor, the force of gravity, asserted itself. Gravity is far too weak to cause single atoms or molecules to cling together but it does dominate large aggregations. In the early universe it was cloud-like masses of hydrogen and helium that had to be drawn inward to widely-spaced centers. It was the great discovery of Newton that the force of gravity falls off according to the square of the distance. The reverse is obvious

Fig. 11-1 Diagrammatic representation of the Big Bang and early history of the universe. The explosion of the highly compressed primeval "atom" depicted at the lower left sent matter and energy speeding into space. So rapid was the expansion of matter-energy that only the simplest elements, hydrogen and helium, had time to form before radiant energy in the form of light had faded. The belt of darkness occupying the central area of the diagram represents the streaming of unorganized matter into an ever-increasing volume of space.

At length the force of gravity began to be effective and thin clouds of hydrogen and helium, the forerunners of the galaxies, began to form. With increasing compaction the central regions of these clouds became self-luminous and light reappeared in the universe. The nature of the first lighted objects of the expanding universe is not known but one theory is that they were the mysterious quasars that are currently the most distant, and hence the oldest, objects known in the universe.

The interval of time from the fading of the Big Bang (evening) through the production of luminous galaxies (morning) to the beginning of a condition of darkness within the galaxies constitutes the first "day" of creation.

the nearer two objects approach each other the greater their mutual attraction.

How any given area of space came to have a greater concentration of matter than nearby areas is only one of the many unsolved problems of galaxy formation. Some have suggested that conditions immediately following the Big Bang created the uneven distribution of matter that later became apparent in the formation of galaxies. In any event innumerable galaxies obviously received allotments of matter sufficient to give rise to billions of bodies like the sun. Our galaxy seems to be no different from millions of others as far as its origin is concerned.

The coming together of an immense aggregation of matter has inevitable results. Although we are only now beginning to understand some of these effects there is no doubt that the generation of heat and light is among them. Certain manifestations of the compaction process are demonstrated by everyday experiences such as the heating of metal by hammering or of air that is forced into a tire. A much more energetic phase of energy release is illustrated by what goes on in the sun. It feeds on nuclear energy, not compaction or combustion. When heat in the center of any large contracting body such as the sun reaches several million degrees nuclear energy begins to be produced and the body becomes self-luminous.

Differences of opinion exist as to when, and where in a youthful galaxy, the first light-producing bodies appear. Some believe that stars may form in the outer zones of a concentrating protogalactic cloud before the center reaches maximum compression. In our own galaxy, for example, a certain class of stars called Population II stars occupy a spherical volume of space that centers in the same core or hub as the streaming spiral arms that make up the more conspicuous part of the configuration. Population I stars are definitely old and clearly formed when the original cloud was spherical and not flattened into its present lens shape.

There may have been Population II stars in the central regions of the galaxy; but, if so, they were destroyed by the continued concentration and reactions of matter there. The question of where in our galaxy the first light began probably cannot be answered. The important fact in the context of the Genesis account is that the first cycle of darkness and light was completed with the lighting up of the galaxy. The first creative day continued until darkness again began to play a role.

COMMENTS AND REFERENCES

Scholars have pondered the meaning of the phrase "and the evening and the morning were the first day." That the same wording should also occur in connection with the second, third, fourth, fifth, and sixth days has been judged to be needless and unduly repetitious. Discussions up to this point should prove that in the creation scriptures no words are wasted or without meaning. The significance of designating each day as being the combination of a period of light and a period of darkness has been discussed in connection with chapters 10 and 11. The problem of this chapter is where in the history of the earth-system the first day of the scriptural account begins.

According to Jewish custom the day begins in the evening as light fades and darkness approaches. If this is truly symbolic of the creation the first day also began as light faded and gave way to darkness. There is indeed such a transition and it is an essential one in the big-bang theory. A suitable place to commence enumeration of the creative days would seem to be when the brilliance of the original great fire-ball was fading away. The succeeding period of universal darkness would thus be the "evening" of the first day while the appearance and dominance of light in the galaxy we call our own would be the "morning" of the first day. As will be apparent in subsequent events this gets us off on the right count or combination of evening-morning or dark-light sequences.

This particular starting point bypasses but does not eliminate much that is important both scripturally and scientifically. The big-bang or initial creation of matter and space is not part of the first day. Likewise, there is nothing whatever to indicate what conditions were like before the big-bang. Most significant of all, the command "let there be light" did not initiate creation; it was uttered long after the heaven and earth of verse 1 had been established.

CHAPTER

12

...LET THERE BE A FIRMAMENT...

And God said, Let there be a firmament in the
midst of the waters, and let it divide the waters
from the waters.

Genesis 1:6

Many problems arise in transforming the words of Genesis
1:6 into a concrete picture of the true relationships of heaven
and earth. Everything depends on how the word firmament is to
be understood. Several broad definitions are available: one
seems to offer the concept of wide open space with practically
nothing in it, the other suggests something localized and solid.
According to the *Oxford English Dictionary*, a respected authority in the origin of words, the term firmament in classical
Latin means "something that strengthens and supports"; a near
synonym is another word meaning a "firm or solid structure."
The Hebrew word probably means "expanse" from the root
raoia. However in Syrian the verb means "to condense, to make
firm or solid." Building on these uncertain ancient roots and
attempting to relate them to modern equivalent words and concepts has been difficult for translators. Usage seems to favor the
idea that the firmament of Genesis is merely the arch or vault of
the sky but the thought that it is also the place where God dwells
is clearly permissible in theological contexts. *The Oxford Dictionary* concludes that in the strict and literal etymological sense

a firmament is: anything which strengthens or supports; a sub-
stratum, or a firm support or foundation.

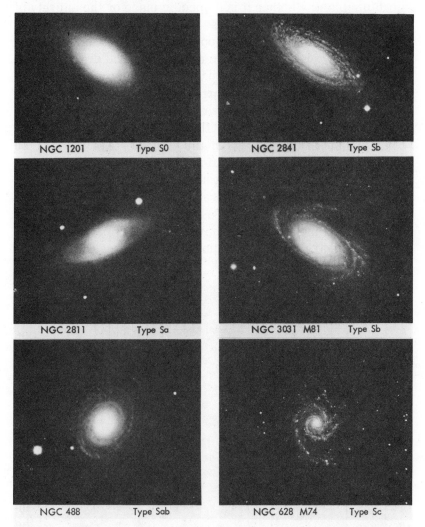

Fig. 12-1   Although there are millions of galaxies and no two are alike they
have the common characteristic of possessing dense luminous cores or hubs.
These photographs illustrate important varieties. The contents of the central
regions and events that take place there were totally mysterious until the invention of x-ray astronomy.

(Courtesy Palomar Observatory, California Institute of Technology.)

A student of Genesis is apparently left to decide whether the firmament is below or above his head, whether it is solid or unsubstantial, and whether it is a specific place or the entirety of space. In choosing among these possibilities ancient thinkers came to what are obviously impossible or nonsense interpretations such as those illustrated in quaint medieval drawings that show the earth as flat and the sky as a transparent hemisphere arching over it and the whole surrounded by water. The findings of astronomy and space exploration prove the impossibility of such reconstructions and it is difficult to believe that they were taught in all seriousness not many centuries ago. It must be realized that thinkers of those times also believed in a flat, immovable earth, in concentric crystalline heavenly spheres, and in the "windows of heaven" as literal truths.

Misinterpretations such as these surrounding biblical references to the firmament have had the effect of creating doubt and distrust in the creation scriptures generally. Critics

Fig. 12-2a   The Andromeda Galaxy (M31). This is the most distant object outside our galaxy visible to the unaided eye. It is similar to the Milky Way Galaxy in many ways and because of its nearness is the best known of the class known as spirals.

(Lick Observatory Photograph.)

and doubters, seemingly in the majority today, contend that Genesis merely puts into words the prevailing misconceptions of ancient times. Believers, on the other hand, are confident that the scriptures are inspired and must somehow be correct even though their correctness is difficult to prove.

As a first step toward reconciliation of modern fact and ancient scripture alternate interpretations of key words and concepts should be given a fair trial. Consider the word firmament was intended to designate the literal heaven where God resides and that it is also a relatively firm and solid place as its ancient root-words clearly imply. This opens up a whole new line of thought which, if followed through to its conclusion, might well remove long-standing misunderstandings of this part of the scriptures.

Fig. 12-2b   An x-ray photograph of the central region of the great Andromeda Galaxy. In visible light this region is a brilliant cloud in which no separate objects are discernable (see Figure 12-2a). When observed by x-rays a collection of massive individual bodies can be detected. This indicates that x-rays from such sources are providing energy to the surrounding gas, which in turn converts it to visible light. This photograph was taken in 1979 by NASA's High Energy Observatory which circles the earth above the atmosphere. (Courtesy NASA.)

Is it possible to learn anything from science that correlates with the theological concept that Heaven is a specific place in space? Man's residence is the planet Earth and it belongs to a number of systems. There is an earth-moon system, a solar system and a galactic system. But there are also other families, orders, or systems of bodies that include the Earth. There are families or groups of sun-like stars—the Pleiades and Ursa Major (Big Dipper) constitute such groupings. The stars in groups like this apparently form simultaneously from the same cloud of matter.

It is well known that the Milky Way Galaxy is part of a system of galaxies called the Local Group. This group consists of our galaxy, the two Magellanic Clouds, the great Adromeda Galaxy and some two dozen other members. Progressing still higher among astronomical orders we find giant clusters of many galaxies. To such aggregations the name supergalaxy is applied. Some of these are enormous by any standard, one cluster in the constellation Coma Berenices is made up of about 10,000 galaxies. One writer has posed the question, "And would there

Fig. 12-3 Galaxies like stars, tend to occur in groups or clusters. This unusual concentration is called Stephan's Quintet.
(Lick Observatory Photograph.)

not be clusters of supergalaxies and clusters of clusters of super-galaxies and so on?" For the time being the design of the universe is a matter of intensive study. How much we may yet learn about it is not evident.

COMMENTS AND REFERENCES

The creation of the Firmament is clearly a very essential step in God's creative work. Attempts to understand and de-scribe what the Firmament is have always been hopelessly entangled with the naive, impossible ideas about the structure of the cosmos that prevailed in ancient times. Modern scholars do not agree as to whether Genesis puts into words the essence of older beliefs or if it, being older, is the ultimate source of these beliefs. What scholars imagine the author(s) of Genesis had in mind is amply illustrated by discussions in *The Interpreters Bible*, p. 472; *The Catholic Biblical Encyclopedia*, p. 367-368; *The New Catholic Encyclopedia*, vol. 5, p. 935; and *The Encyclopedia of Biblical Interpretation* (Jewish), vol. on Genesis 1.

Events that led to the irrevocable decline and abandonment of ancient and medieval ideas about the cosmos are well de-scribed in Stephen Toulmin and Jane Goodfield, 1965, *The Discovery of Time*, Harper and Row; same authors, 1961, *The Fabric of the Heavens*, Harper; J. C. Greene, 1959, *The Death of Adam*, Mentor Books; Arthur Koestler, 1959, *The Sleepwalkers*, Grosset and Dunlap; and C. C. Gillispie, 1959, *Genesis and Geology*, Harper.

Although modern scholars may understand perfectly well what pre-scientific peoples imagined about the Firmament neither ancient nor modern thinkers have examined all possible meanings. Modern discoveries clearly justify the thought that the Firmament is the center or hub of a galaxy such as our own Milky Way.

13

...GOD DIVIDED THE WATERS...

And God made the firmament, and divided the
waters which were *under the* firmament from the
waters which were above the *firmament:* and it
was so.

Genesis 1:7

God called the firmament Heaven and Heaven is where he
resides. These are scriptural verities. The location of Heaven is
not revealed in the Bible but it could well be the center of our
galaxy. This conclusion is reached by an indirect line of reasoning that has been partly explained in the preceding chapter.

Our galaxy is a great astronomical aggregation embracing
the earth, sun and countless other bodies. It has a center or core
around which all these revolve. Sufficient to say that a scientific
description of the galaxy as a whole lends credibility to the conclusion that the Firmament (Heaven) is at the center of our Milky
Way Galaxy. Assuming that this is so, what is to be understood
by the reference to waters under the firmament and waters
above the firmament? Being earthbound creatures we immediately think in earthbound terms. Above is anything existing
above the surface or away from the center of the earth. Below is
downward toward the surface or center of the earth. We usually
accept the surface of the earth or our own position on it as a

Fig. 13-1 An artist's interpretation of the appearance of our galaxy as seen from a hypothetical planet in nearby space. The configuration of the central core and spiral arms is based on information obtained from radio-wave astronomy.

(Painting by and permission to use courtesy of William Hartmann.)

reference when we think of anything being under or above. It is simply upward or downward from the surface or ourselves on the surface. Gravity, ever with us, helps tell what is up and down and thus above or below us.

Our earth-bound frame of reference is obviously of great use in everyday thinking but of no use when we move away from the earth. In absolute rather than relative terms what is down to the inhabitants of Salt Lake City is up to those of Brisbane, Australia.

As I write this I have before me one of the famous space photos of the Earth, taken by the Apollo astronauts. Here is the earth hanging in space against a background of uniform darkness—nothing else visible. I search the globe for landmarks for there are patches of land showing through the cover of swirling clouds. I locate part of the familiar coastlines of Africa because the ruddy desert here contrasts with the dark oceans and there are fewer clouds over the land. Then I automatically shift the photo so that north is up in my view. Now I can see other outlines —I have become oriented. I have adjusted my view to a frame of reference without really thinking how that frame of reference came into being and what it means when we are on the earth or far from it in distant space.

The astronauts found when far from earth and its gravity field that familiar terms such as up and down, below and above, north and south became meaningless. Only when they decided on some celestial object as a reference point could they even describe their surroundings. This is the problem astronomers have had to solve in an arbitrary way as they map and describe the heavens. They have solved the problem by projecting the system used on earth into the celestial sphere. Thus the north celestial pole is a point in the heavens toward which the north pole of the earth is pointing. There is also a celestial equator that hangs directly over the terrestrial one. The earth and sky are like two great globes, the former inside the latter and both divisible in terms of latitude and longitude, into degrees, minutes and seconds. Just as a remote spot in the ocean can be located by this grid system so can the faintest star in heaven be pin-pointed on the celestial sphere.

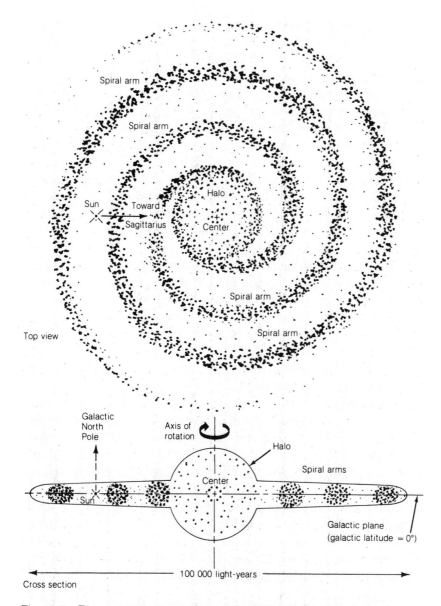

Fig. 13-2   Diagrammatic views of our galaxy. Upper drawing shows the configuration of central core, halo, and spiral arms. Lower view is a cross-section
showing the same features. The position of the sun is emphasized. The galaxy
is 100,000 light years across and contains an estimated 1,500,000,000 stars.
(NASA.)

Certainly it was a natural tendency or even necessity of thinking in earth-bound terms that led to earlier interpretations of the scriptures under discussion. There are many ancient and medieval illustrations that purport to show waters above the earth (clouds, rain, etc.) and waters below the earth (in subterranean caves and reservoirs).

The obvious impossibility of these interpretations, as proved by space exploration and by a better understanding of the structure of the earth, is one reason why literal interpretations of the scripture have fallen into disrepute. But the scriptures may be strengthened, not weakened, by alternate choices of a few key words and phrases. The waters above and under the firmament are not the waters of the earth, they are the waters of space already described in chapter 7.

May we return briefly for a moment to the thought that the firmament (Heaven) is in the center of the galaxy and consider how the structure of this great system might be described in a simple understandable way? Our galaxy is not unusual; there are other examples by the thousands making up the class of galaxies that have two curving spiral arms lying in one plane. The discovery that we live in a spiral galaxy is one of the triumphs of modern astronomy.

Since galactic arms occur almost without exception in opposite, identical, and symmetrical pairs they might be distinguished by comparing their locations with respect to their common center of rotation. Thus they could be identified as being right and left, to the north or south, up and down, or above and below. On the face of it one choice appears to be as good as another. In the scripture the problem of describing the galaxy is solved neatly enough by referring to one of the arms as being *above* the firmament, the other *under* the firmament. This scheme makes it possible to specify the location of the matter and space that would later become the solar system and the earth.

COMMENTS AND REFERENCES

The most abundant type of galaxy has a spiral shape with two symmetrically coiling arms springing from opposite sides of a central hub or bulge. Our home galaxy is of this type. The purpose of this chapter is to draw attention to the fact that Genesis 1:7 can be interpreted in terms of this typical configuration.

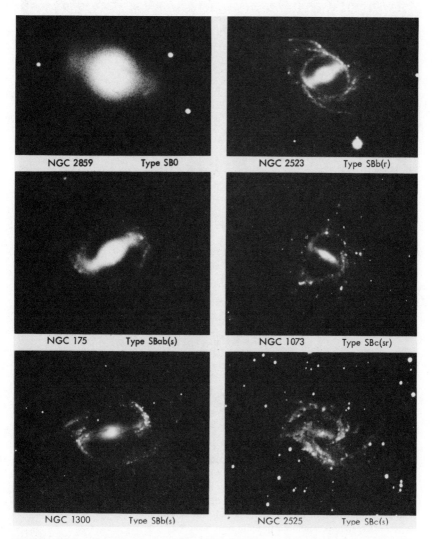

Fig. 13-3 Illustrations of barred galaxies. This type is characterized by oppositely directed extensions of the central core. These bars rotate with the center like a solid wheel. Commonly, the outermost ends of the bars give rise to spiral forms that lag behind the general rotation. Some astronomers believe that barred galaxies represent a stage leading to spiral types.

(Palomar Observatory, California Institute of Technology.)

Fig. 13-4   A spiral galaxy that clearly shows the typical central core and op-positely placed curving symmetrical arms. Many knots or "gatherings" are visible. This fine example is in the constellation Pisces.

(Palomar Observatories California Institute of Technology.)

Galactic structure is one of the major mysteries of astronomy. The over-all shape of a spiral galaxy suggests that the center is rotating at a relatively rapid rate and that material composing the arms is lagging or streaming behind. While it is true that spiral galaxies do rotate, this is clearly not the full explanation of the arms and their variations. Many books and articles discuss the problems of galactic structure and motion: W. Becker and G. Contopoulos (eds.), 1970, "The Spiral Structure of Our Galaxy," International Astronomical Union Symposium, no. 38, Springer-Verlag; Gerrit L. Verschour and Kenneth I. Kellermann (eds.), "Galactic and Extra-Galactic Radio Astronomy," Springer-Verlag; Bart J. Bok, 1972, "Updating Galactic Spiral Structure," in *American Scientist*, vol. 60, pp. 709-722; Richard B. Larsen, 1977, "The Origin of Galaxies," in *American Scientist*, vol. 65, no. 2.

Interesting as the subject of the origin and shape of galaxies may be, it need not be intensively studied or thoroughly understood in order to judge the possible significance of interpreting this part of Genesis on the basis of galactic shapes alone.

14

... EVENING AND MORNING
... SECOND DAY

And the evening and the morning were the second day.

Genesis 1:8

Accord ing to Genesis the second day of creation produced the Firmament. The account is brief but the implied action is inconceivably vast and complex. Assuming that our method of correlating scripture and cosmology is correct the production of the Firmament is equivalent to events that followed the production of the first light-producing objects of the galaxy. Scripturally, we find ourselves dealing with events between the production of light on the first day and the appearance of Earth on the third day. Cosmologically, we are between the initial condensation of a protogalaxy from hydrogen and helium and the appearance of a solar system in the arm of a fully developed spiral galaxy. Looked at from any viewpoint these are staggering vistas and in the present state of knowledge little beyond speculations can be offered.

The situation is this: We know our Milky Way system is a spiral galaxy but it is extremely difficult to learn much about the details of its construction. Our solar system is embedded so deeply in a mass of stars, dust and gas that we are literally prevented from seeing very far in any direction. We have a clear case of not being able to see the forest for the trees—we cannot see the galaxy for the stars. We have had particular difficulty in locating the center of our system. We can perceive the Milky Way and be convinced that it is a band or disk of numerous stars, but a clearly dominating center is not apparent to the naked eye. As late as 1910 astronomers placed the sun at the center and it was not until 1935 that we correctly localized our system about two-thirds of the way from the center to the edge. Our best clues come from study of the relatively close Andromeda galaxy and other spirals that display a broader veiw of things.

We perceive that the spiral patterns of galaxies show great variety and that no two are identical. On the other hand the cores of all galaxies are superficially the same, appearing as brilliantly lighted spherical forms within which no details can be made out. It is evident that the cores contain most of the material of their respective systems. Still more important, the arms, regardless of their varied shapes, are mere appendages of the cores and have obviously originated by processes operating in the central regions.

Astronomers speak of the mystery of the galactic nucleus. It is mysterious because great quantities of radiation are generated there from sources and by processes that are very poorly understood. Although visible light from the energetic central core is almost entirely blocked out by dust it is possible to measure radiation in the form of infrared, radio, and gamma rays. These, because of their longer wave lengths, can pass through the dust clouds to be detected by suitable instruments on earth.

What emerges is that energy equal to that produced by thousands of suns is pouring out from a relatively small area, about 3.26 light years across. It is calculated that the mass of matter in the core is equal to 1 or 2 million suns. There is also evidence that great explosive events take place in the core. One of these, estimated to have occurred about 10,000,000 years ago, released more energy than that produced in the lifetime of 1,000 suns. Hydrogen gas produced by this explosion is speeding outward into the spiral arms but is still a long way from the solar system.

The production of so much radiant energy from so small a

Fig. 14-1   Artist's conception of a black hole. Matter spiralling into the central vortex becomes so concentrated and gravity so powerful that nothing, not even light, can escape. Most astronomers believe black holes are theoretically possible, and many regard them as absolutely necessary to explain conditions in galactic centers. In spite of this, no black holes have yet been positively identified in space.

The significance of a black hole in the history of a galaxy such as the one that produced the earth is that it creates a period of darkness that passes into a period of light to fulfill the requirement of the second day of creation. Unsolved as yet is the problem of how, if ever, matter is released from confinement to again become luminous. Some believe the black hole merely evaporates, others favor the concept of an explosive event.

(Hansen Planetarium, Salt Lake City.)

space has not been explained. Comparison with other galaxies merely compounds the mystery. The Andromeda galaxy, in many ways a sister to our own, has a similar small nucleus that outshines the rest of the galaxy. Here also are evidences of occasional explosive events. What goes on in galaxies such as ours is mild compared with what is observed in other aggregations such as Seyfert galaxies and quasars!

It is informative to note the diversity of opinion that exists among astronomers as to what it is that activates galactic centers. A popular textbook, copyrighted in 1979, lists the explosion of enormous unstable "stars" 500 to 1,000 times more massive than the sun, the actual bodily collision of stars, and the accretion of gas and dust onto high density, high gravity objects.

Fig. 14-2   Barred galaxies such as this example in the constellation Eridanus are regarded as representing a stage in the formation of the more common spiral types. The so-called bars that spring in opposite directions from the core seem to be the result of an explosive event, perhaps the destruction of a black hole. Subsequent rotation of the core and bars produces the curving spiral configurations farther out.

Another textbook (1975) ignores other possible explanations in favor of the black hole theory. The author comments that a galactic black hole "might have masses equal to 100 million suns and would be half a billion miles in diameter!"

Possibilities listed in an article in a foremost scientific journal (1977) include giant superstars, a black hole, giant pulsars, colliding star swarms, and multiple supernovas. A more recent (July 1980) article in the same journal lists an ongoing series of closely packed supernovas, the impact of cosmic rays with closely spaced interstellar matter, an abundance of pulsars, a large black hole, and an abundance of small black holes.

Simply because they are so frequently mentioned black holes are obviously being taken seriously by astronomers who theorize about galactic energy sources. It is difficult to reconcile the destruction of matter in black holes with the production of energy in the same general areas. There must be a connection but no one seems to understand what it is. White holes have been visualized as sites from which matter and energy emerge and "worm" holes are suggested as tunnel-like connections between black holes and white holes. Many minds are working to solve the black hole problem.

When astronomers know all there is to know about the center of the galaxy they will furnish us with a solution to the mystery of how the Firmament of the second day of creation came into being. Meanwhile we join them in speculation. Our view of each of the creative days is that periods of darkness must be succeeded by periods of light. Certainly a black hole appears to be exactly what is needed for the dark phase of the second day. Here, more dramatically than any other known arrangement, light is separated from darkness. The separation is forceable — light is restrained from escaping and that is what makes a black hole what it is. But this solves only half of the problem.

In order to complete the second creative day darkness must give way to light. This requirement could be met by the destruction of a black hole. But we have no evidence that light ever escapes from black holes or that they disappear explosively from the scene. We do know that violent events are taking place in the galactic core and that it is an extremely luminous area. Furthermore, we suspect that explosive events initiate the formation of the spiral arms. For our purposes the creation of the Firmament may be considered to have been completed when spiral arms appear. At this stage the second day of our particular system was over and the third day began.

...GATHERED TOGETHER
UNTO ONE PLACE...

And God said, Let the waters under the heaven
be *gathered together unto one place,* and let the
dry land appear: and it was so.

Genesis 1:9

T he gathering of waters into one place, which is the topic of
this chapter, is an essential step in the preparation of the earth.
However, this step is logical and right only if the major conclusions of previous chapters are acceptable. One essential premise
is that the waters referred to are not the water bodies of the
planet Earth but are, instead, the unorganized material of interstellar space, portions of which are rich in water as such
(Chapter 7). A second premise is that the waters under the
firmament and the waters above the firmament refer to the two
opposite spiral arms of the galaxy (Chapter 13).

Building on the assumption that these conclusions are basically correct the next step follows logically. Note the expression
waters *under* the heavens, not the waters *above* the heavens.
This wording neatly makes known that the scene of action is
being restricted to a specific area of space, namely one part of a
two-part system. What goes on across space in the opposite arm
of the galaxy no longer enters the picture.

Further restrictions become evident. Although it might be
inferred from the brief wording of the text that *all* the waters on

one side of the galaxy were gathered into one place this is not necessarily so. A very small part of the original cloud suffices to produce an entire solar system. One thing that seems to exist in overwhelming sufficiency is matter. The text does not specify that the segregated material was to become the earth only. In its initial form the original "gathering" may have been material for the entire solar system, or even a local system of a number of stars. The emphasis is on a process that would eventually give rise to the earth.

The whole process of formation and evolution of astronomical bodies of all magnitudes from groups of galaxies through single galaxies, star groups, individual stars, planets and satellites may be thought of in terms of successive accretions or "gatherings." Astronomers recognize different processes which might be included in the comprehensive term "gathering." These are mostly self-explanatory: gravitational attraction, accretion, and condensation. The process was ongoing and very complex.

Fig. 15-1   Many knots or "gatherings" are visible in the arms of this spiral galaxy. Any of these aggregations contains enough matter for many solar systems.

(Lowell Observatory Photograph.)

The material for the galaxies had to be segregated early in the history of the universe; this was followed by condensations within the galaxies which were destined to become individual star systems or groups of related stars. Still later the material of the stellar systems underwent condensations so that individual stars, binary twins or complex planetary systems were produced. Finally, many planets show the effects of continuing accretionary processes whereby their satellite systems came into being. For example, the Earth and Moon are thought to have formed from the same dust and gas cloud. Juptier and Saturn with their satellites are miniature solar systems each having formed from its separate cloud.

An interesting description of the final gathering together of earth materials appears in an excellent book, *Planetary Geology*, by Nicholas M. Short (Prentice-Hall, 1975).

Details of the processes by which the planets grew from the solar nebula are still inferential. Clots of matter probably built up into tiny planetesimals held together by frozen ammonia, or water, organic matter, and magnetic or electrical charges. The initial aggregation may have resulted from random collisions in turbulent vortices in the cloud or from faster-moving particles overtaking slower ones in the path-crossing ellipitical orbits that prevailed in the rotating disc. At first the planetesimals were probably only meters in size but as individuals reached critical masses they began to have significant gravitational effects on their neighbors and thus attracted smaller particles into themselves. Growth rates increased with time—the initial clots formed in less than 100,000 years; asteroidal-sized bodies took no more than 10 million years; the entire planetary system reached its present dimensions in less than 100 million years. Eventually, the larger bodies, growing at the expense of the smaller ones, swept up so much of the remaining materials that only a few planet-sized aggregates were left (pp. 51-52).

The history of each aggregation regardless of its size or present relationships began when its component materials were "gathered in one place." Before its separation each entity was a part of something larger; afterward it had its own individuality.

Very little appears to be added or subtracted to most astronomical bodies once their basic materials are separated from the constituents that are destined to become other bodies. Astronomical birth is like the birth of an organism—it is the event which separates offspring from parent and starts it on a separate course. Each entity has a time of birth and it is from this moment that its history and the calculation of its age begins. It is the nature of the universe that galaxies, suns, and even planets must run their separate courses mostly in solitary isolation. There may be reactions between bodies across the reaches of space it is true but exchange of material is practically non-existent.

Observation teaches that astronomical bodies of all types evolve and change after their segregation. That which commences as a disorganized mass of gas and dust may condense into a much smaller space to become a galaxy; lightless and shapeless clumps of matter within galaxies in turn become self-luminous stars; rotating disks of gas and dust attending newly formed stars are segregated into the rings or clouds destined to become planets or satellites. Wandering remnants may condense to asteroids or comets or remain as grains of dust. What an object contains and its location at the time it begins its separate existence largely determines what it ultimately becomes. Although all essential elements are in each shapeless, unorganized cloud at its beginning, the final product will not emerge until much later. Nevertheless, under the operation of law, the final outcome is strictly predetermined by what originally enters into each packet of matter.

The theme of Genesis 1:9 is clearly the emergence of a solid planet from formerly diffuse, unorganized material. The formation of the earth has always been a topic of great interest to geologists and astronomers and one to which they have devoted a great deal of attention. After all, we do have the end product, the solid earth, for first-hand study and are rapidly gleaning from other nearby astronomical bodies information that is important to understanding the origin of our home planet. A very brief synopsis of the history of theories of the origin of the solar system may not be out of place.

The first serious attempt to explain the origin of the solar system was in 1644 when the French philosopher Rene Descartes proposed that it all began as a cloud of unorganized primordial matter. The sun and planets, he believed, were formed from great eddies or swirls within the initial cloud. In 1755 Immanuel Kant elaborated and refined the nebular theory by taking into account the laws of gravity that had been propounded by Newton in 1687. Kant, by combining the idea of spiral motion and gravitational attraction, came up with a surprisingly good model for the origin of the solar system.

Other theories of the solar system have been proposed over the centuries but none of any consequence commences with anything basically different from the nebulous aggregation of matter visualized by Descartes. How the original material passed from its diffuse condition as gas and dust to large solid bodies has always been the greatest problem.

To achieve the successively more dense aggregations that constitute the sun, planets and satellites it is necessary to visualize various processes whereby portions of matter are separated or gathered out of larger masses. It is with regard to the segregating processes that the various nebular theories differ from each other. As chemistry and physics have provided more sophisticated understanding of the laws governing such processes the successive theories have clearly become more satisfactory and believable.

For larger entities at least, gravity seems entirely able to accomplish the drawing together and compression of matter that resulted in the solar system. Some theories would produce the sun first and then the planets; others would form the planets first and the sun later. Even so, both classes of theories begin with a mass of dust and gas which has already undergone condensation and commenced to rotate about its center of gravity. One view is that essentially all the original material became concentrated in a single central sun or star. According to the law of conservation of angular momentum the speed of rotation increases as the material is drawn together in such a body. Speed of rotation is the critical factor of this theory for it is the excessive speed of the central contracting sun which is supposed to give rise to the

Fig. 15-2 Stages in the formation of the solar system. Above, the original nebula of slowly contracting gas and dust; middle, intermediate stage with the center a compact self-luminous body and outlying material forming into rings; lower, the fully formed system with the sun, shining by thermonuclear reaction, in the center and a variety of solid and gaseous planets in orbits about it.

(Hansen Planetarium, Salt Lake City, Utah.)

planets. It is known on theoretical grounds that when the speed of a liquid body reaches a certain limit it will begin to spill out or lose material from the most rapidly rotating equatorial zone. This will take the form of a thin ring or rings somewhat resembling the rings of Saturn. It is from this material spilled out of the sun that the planets, according to the theory, are derived. Enough rings, each of somewhat different composition, are supposed to have been produced to form the separate planets. By complex systems of eddies and currents the material of each ring was subsequently condensed into its respective planet. A great difficulty with this theory is that the central sun in now rotating far too slowly to give off rings and there is little evidence that it ever had the necessary velocity to do so in the past.

Theories of a second class are more popular today and seem to satisfy more of the known facts. Again the initial material is a diffuse, flattened, slowly rotating cloud of dust and gas. As the material draws together, irregular clouds or knots of material are left behind while the greater bulk continues to spiral slowly inward. It is the material left behind that becomes the planets. An attractive feature of this theory is that it explains why there are two distinct groups of planets and why each planet is different from the others. Members of the outer group, Jupiter, Saturn, Uranus and Neptune, are larger, mostly gaseous, and have large numbers of satellites. The inner group, Mercury, Venus, Earth and Mars—are small, dense, heavy and have few satellites.

According to this theory the material for the outer, larger, gaseous planets was left behind before the sun came into existence as the governing central body. These giant outer planets may, in fact, have approximately the composition of the parent nebula at the time they became separated from it. Now that spacecraft have passed near Jupiter and have obtained much data as to its structure and composition we are able to make more reliable comparisons with the Earth and the distant outer planets.

It is supposed that some time between the detachment of the material of Jupiter and that of the inner planets the sun became a self-luminous body in the center of the system. By this is meant that the central material had become so tightly packed and dense that nuclear reactions began. When a temperature of 15,000,000° C is reached light and other radiation is produced and a shining star results. From this stage onward the sun would have dominated the formation and history of planets. The solar wind was increasingly important. This is the outward-pressing stream of light and other radiation which exerts a measurable pressure upon anything it encounters. The tails of comets are good examples of its effects. It is thought possible that the solar

Fig. 15-3 The Rosette Nebula. The wide circular belt of glowing matter appears to be expanding outward due to radiation pressure from the intensely brilliant stars in the central region. Only relatively heavy particles could resist such pressure and remain in the near vicinity of these stars.
(Courtesy Palomar Observatory, California Institute of Technology.)

wind was effective in dispersing or sweeping away the lighter gaseous molecules near the sun so as to leave behind relatively more of the heavier elements such as silicon and iron. It is an abundance of these elements which characterizes the inner planets. By contrast the outer gaseous planets are rich in hydrogen and helium.

The present system is thought to have been in existence for almost 5 billion years during which time the sun has not only driven away much of its surrounding atmospheric cloud but also has burned away a great deal of its own substance. In earlier stages, the burning was very energetic and the sun was much hotter and brighter than it is now. The burning process literally "cleaned up" the solar system by sweeping away the remnants of the nebular cloud. This was the final event which brought the planet earth into existence as a separate solid body. The earth had at length "come up dry."

COMMENTS AND REFERENCES

The ninth verse of Genesis 1 seems to be the first scripture pertaining specifically to the solar system and planet Earth. The modern view is that the Earth emerged as a culmination of successive gatherings or condensations. The processes by which the materials of galaxies segregated from a universal cloud, how the solar nebula condensed within the Milky Way Galaxy and how the sun and planets gathered from the solar nebula are subjects of intense inquiry and speculation.

Books that deal with the problem of segregation or condensation include T. De Jong and M. Maedor, 1977, *Star Formation*, International Astronomical Union Symposium, No. 75, R. Reidel Publishing Co.; Clark R. Chapman, 1977, *The Inner Planets*, Scribner; C. G. Walker, 1977, *Origin of the Atmosphere*, Macmillan; Robert Jastrow and A. G. Cameron, 1963, *Origin of the Solar System*, Academic Press.

An entire issue of *Scientific American*, Sept. 1975, vol. 33, no. 3 is devoted to the solar system. This is a readable and well illustrated introduction to the system to which Earth belongs. Another excellent source is *New Frontiers in Astronomy*, a com-

pilation of articles from the *Scientific American,* with an introduction by Owen Gingerich, 1975. Another selection of *Scientific
American* papers is "Planet Earth," Freeman, 1974. Bibliog-
raphies of these sources open up practically all aspects of
modern astronomy and earth science.

CHAPTER

16

...LET THE DRY LAND
(EARTH) APPEAR...

And God said, Let the waters under the heaven
be gathered together unto one place, and *let the
dry land appear:* and it was so.
And God called the dry land Earth; . . .
                                        Genesis 1:9-10

The time-honored interpretation of Genesis 1:9-10 is that it describes the creation of the major land and water features of the planet Earth. A special point is made of the "waters" being gathered unto one place. The picture of a single great continent emerging from the waters of the ocean is entirely compatible with the early earthbound concept of creation. But there are several good reasons to question the assumption that the scriptural passages referred to apply to features of the planet Earth. As argued in chapters 7 and 13 it is more probable that the word "waters" designates the cloud of gas and dust from which the various astronomical bodies including the planet Earth emerged. These arguments need not be repeated here. We turn to the manner in which the term earth is used in Genesis 1. Why is the word Earth capitalized in verse 10 of Genesis while in previous verses it is not capitalized? Both the capitalized and uncapitalized form seem to come from the same Greek word, *rets*.

Fig. 16-1 Earth in space as photographed from the moon. Both continents and oceans are plainly evident. Genesis 1:9-10 offers the choice of believing that the reference to "dry land" applies only to the continents of the planet or to the entire Earth.

(Courtesy NASA.)

If there is any verse of Genesis which seems to refer specifically to the planet it is verse 10. If the capitalized term "Earth" is
indeed the entire planet then the "dry land" referred to in verse
9 must also be the same because God himself "called the dry land
Earth." There is the distinct impression that God is here giving a
name to the planet and not to the materials of which it is composed.

There are other arguments in favor of the thought that the
earth or dry land referred to in the scripture is the entire globe
and not the superficial land masses on its surface. If all the
waters of the planet Earth were in one place they would constitute an ocean much larger than the Pacific. It is difficult to conceive of such an extensive sheet or shell of water as being "in one
place," as it would have to encircle a large part of the earth. A
field of alfalfa is not in one place as much as is a haystack.

May we now attempt a new interpretation of the verses
which tell of the appearance of the dry land or earth? Assume
that what is being described is the formation of the solar system
and the earth, not the shaping of continents and oceans. We are
told that God ordered the waters under heaven to be gathered

Fig. 16-2   God dividing the water from the dry land. The artist depicts the
traditional view that the waters and land referred to in Genesis 1:9-10 are
features of the planet Earth.
(Painting by Raffaello Santi, 16th Century.)

unto one place. As an extension of this thought the coming together of the material that would in time become the solar system is also well described as a gathering. We have already made the point that "the waters under the heavens" probably refer to certain material in our arm of the galaxy. We follow good astronomical theory in visualizing the beginning of the solar system as a gathering together of some of this material. The scriptural language might be interpreted to mean that *all* the water under the heavens were gathered together in one place, but that only part of the material was thus localized is not ruled out. In any event the gathering together "in one place" seems to be a very acceptable description of the accumulation of matter in a specific region of space that is an essential step in the formation of a solar system and also in the formation of individual planets and satellites.

Thus we come at length to undoubted references to the planet Earth. Genesis reads: "... let the dry land appear: ...." Following the arguments just presented it is not difficult to visualize the planet emerging from enclosing mists or clouds. The references to "dry land" or a dry earth is scientifically very significant. The use of this wording forces the conclusion that the earth was at one stage without surface bodies of liquid water. If anyone has lingering doubts about the thought of a dry earth he should consider the opening event of the 7th day where the statement is made that there had been no rain up to that time. Admittedly there could be oceans without rain but such an arrangement raises additional problems that do not exist if there were no oceans.

Now that we know a great deal about other planets that are our neighbors in space we perceive that the existence of a watery planet is unusual. The Moon is now waterless and apparently always has been; Mercury shows no evidence of water whatsoever. The water on Mars at the present time is locked within the surface material, frozen in ice, or vaporized in the atmosphere. Venus appears too hot to support surface water or ice. Currently no one believes that there is enough water as such on any of these planets to greatly affect what goes on there and certainly not enough to support higher forms of life. One of the terms descriptive of these bodies is that they are dry. Furthermore, judging by the examples we have, it is more likely that a planet will "come up dry" than that it will emerge supplied with bodies of surface water.

Putting off for the time being a discussion of how the earth received its presently bounteous supply of surface water it is interesting to consider why it must have been dry at the beginning. There are several possible explanations: water may not have been available as such among the components that were then existing on or within the planet; water may have been in existence but only in frozen or gaseous form; water may have been lost or driven off by excessive heat derived either from the earth or from the sun. Evidence that the earth passed through a molten stage favors the last named explanation.

Fig. 16-3   The waterless surface of Mercury as photographed by Mariner 10 spacecraft in 1974.
(Courtesy NASA.)

The best evidence for such a molten phase is the fact that the earth consists of a series of great shells or spheres arranged according to density. In other words the heavier material is found in the very dense core of iron and nickle or heavier metals; this is overlaid by the mantle composed of iron, magnesium and silicon averaging six to eleven times as heavy as water; the outer shell of the solid earth, commonly called the crust, has an average density two to three times that of water. Resting on the solid earth is the watery shell or hydrosphere and above this the various atmospheric levels ranging from dense to very light outward. The most logical explanation for this layered arrangement is that there must have been a time when heavy constituents of a complex original mixture could sink and light materials could rise freely to assume a position of equilibrium. The separation of milk and cream furnishes a simple analogy.

It should be stated that not all earth scientists and astronomers agree in the necessity of a molten earth. Some believe that the layered arrangement is an original feature—the heavier material was gathered from space first, the successively lighter constituents being added as time went on. At no time was there complete melting and mixing. The truth may lie somewhere between the ideas of a completely cold beginning and a completely hot one. No one doubts that the outer part of the core of the earth is now molten. Is it in process of cooling or in process of heating? No other planet appears to have a molten core such as the earth. This is based on the fact that the magnetic and electrical fields of the earth are much stronger than those of any other solid body so far investigated.

It is also known that a very hot plastic zone exists within the upper part of the earth's mantle from about 100 to 400 miles beneath the surface. This is called the *asthenosphere* and it is considered to be the source of much if not most of the volcanic material that appears at the surface. The upper solid layer, or *lithosphere*, rests very uneasily upon the plastic material and in fact slides about upon it to create vast earth movements that are continually altering the major surface features. Strangest of all is the discovery that the outer shell is being engulfed into the plastic layer and gradually destroyed along certain geologically active zones. This whole topic of what goes on at the surface and near the surface of the earth is an intensely interesting one that we cannot discuss here. Many good references are available.

The important point is that the earth is partly molten at the present time and has apparently been so for many geologic ages. No other planet has such an active history and except for Mars there is little evidence for much internal heat being generated or displayed by volcanic action. The landscapes of the other planets are very ancient and have remained unchanged since their formation. The surface of the earth, by contrast, is continually being altered and reorganized.

In the minds of most geologists the earth is what it is— active and changing—because of the heat energy it generates and contains. This same heat energy may have been much greater in the past and would then have been sufficient to either prevent the accumulation of water or to drive off any that might have been present on the surface. In order to escape the gravitational pull of the earth a water molecule would have to possess a store of energy sufficient to give an average velocity of 11.2 kilometers per second. This is well within that which would be imparted by the temperature that would exist if the surface of the globe were molten lava which ranges between 700° C and 1200° C.

One more agent may have been at work to create an originally "dry" earth. This is the so-called solar wind or radiation pressure. As the name suggests, a force is exerted by the stream of powerful radiation (including light) that arises from the sun. The combination of rays and particles is sufficiently powerful to actually push molecules and small particles away from the sun. This incidentally is the force which shapes and directs the outward streaming tails of comets as they enter the central regions of the solar system. During the earlier history of the system there is good reason to believe that the sun was hotter and more powerful in every way. At this time the solar wind could well have been sufficient to strip away and disperse all the lighter molecules, including water, that were produced from within or were attached by gravity to the earth.

Scriptures do not specify that the earth was originally either hot or cold. That it had to be hot in order to be dry is no great

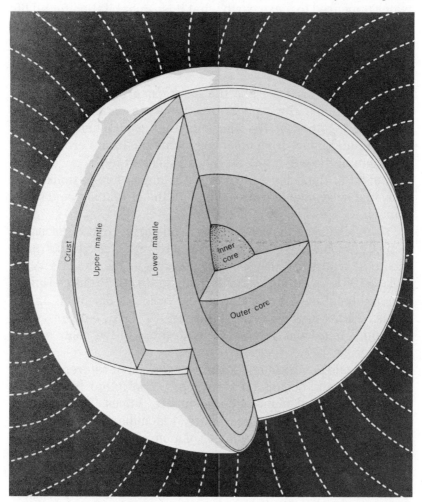

Fig. 16-4   Structure of the earth according to current geophysical theory. The core is thought to be mostly iron, the mantle a mixture of heavy silicate materials, and the crust, of which we have ample samples, is lighter minerals and rocks rich in oxygen. The hydrosphere and atmosphere complete the shell-like layering from the heaviest at the center to the lightest on the exterior. The dashed lines represent the earth's magnetic field.

(Courtesy United States Geological Survey.)

obstacle to interpreting the scripture. The important part is that it "came up dry." Later as both science and scripture affirm water appeared to make earth what it is—a habitation for all life including man.

COMMENTS AND REFERENCES

This chapter describes the emergence of the Earth as a separate planet. Its appearance was essentially the final gathering together of the elements that would henceforth be separate and apart from other aggregations. In the broad sense the origin of the earth was merely an incident in the ongoing development of the solar system and it is impossible to think of its early history except in connection with the parent sun and sister planets.

The history of the solar system and early earth is discussed in most textbooks of geology and planetology. A suggested reference that traces the pre-planetary origins of the earth is W. L. Stokes, 1981, *Essentials of Earth History*, 4th ed., Prentice-Hall. A compilation of many excellent papers from the *Scientific American* is "Planet Earth," W. H. Freeman, 1974. An entire issue of *Scientific American*, Sept. 1975, is devoted to the solar system and its origin.

The solid earth cannot be discussed without reference to the atmosphere and oceans that envelop it. Books that bear on the origin of the total planetary system are: James C. G. Walker, 1977, *Evolution of the Atmosphere*, Macmillan; Peter J. Brancazio, 1964, *The Origin and Evolution of Atmospheres and Oceans*, Wiley; and Robert Jastrow and A. G. Cameron, 1963, *Origin of the Solar System*, Academic Press.

Other books and articles deal with more specific topics: V. S. Safronov, 1972, *Evolution of the Proplanetary Cloud and Formation of the Earth and Planets*, Israel Program for Scientific Translations, Jerusalem; Hubert Reeves, ed., 1972, *Symposium on the Origin of the Solar System*, Edition du Centre National de la Recherche Scientifique, Paris; Lawrence Grossman and John W. Larimer, 1974, "Chemical History of the Solar System," in *Reviews of Geophysics and Space Physics*, vol. 12, no. 1.

17

...GRASS...HERB...
TREE...THE THIRD DAY

And God said, Let the earth bring forth *grass,*
the *herb* yielding seed, and the fruit *tree* yielding
fruit after his kind, whose seed is in itself, upon
the earth: and it was so.

And the earth brought forth grass, and herb
yielding seed after his kind, and the tree yielding
fruit, whose seed was in itself, after his kind:
and God saw that it was good.

And the evening and the morning were *the
third day.*

Genesis 1:11-13

T he bringing forth of plant life was a major work of the third
creative period. Genesis says the earth "brought forth" (past
time) as if the event followed the command immediately; however, looking ahead to Genesis 2:5-6, one may surmise that what
is said in Genesis 1 is in reference to the organization of matter in
preparation for future earth life. The account mentions grass,
trees, and herbs, probably to make clear that *all* plant life is to be
included. Certainly we can excuse the omission of the seaweeds
and microscopic algae of which ancient peoples had no knowledge and for which they had no names.

The puzzle of the creation of plant life is that it comes before
the organization of the heavenly bodies including the "greater

light that rules the day." How could plant life exist before the sun was in existence? A basic fact of nature is that plants cannot exist in the absence of light. In scientific terms plants cannot live without photosynthesis. What point would there be in producing plants on earth before the basic energy source of the solar system was operating. This is such a hopeless reversal of the common-sense order of things that one would, on the face of it, conclude that the writer of Genesis was inconceivably ignorant or inexcusably careless of the facts. It is such an obvious mistake, one might say, that it appears almost deliberate. Is it a signal thrown up for a purpose? If accepted as an outright error it alone is sufficient to discourage a scientist from placing much weight on Genesis as a textbook of natural history. If it is not an error it bears careful looking into.

Looking ahead to Genesis 2:5 where there is the strong implication that plants did not grow on earth until the seventh day we may infer that what happened on the third day was in preparation for their future appearance. No such stipulation is made regarding the sun, moon and stars which were also products of the third day. They did actually appear then.

This is in line with a basic message of the creation scriptures: Inanimate things were organized and finished in the first six periods while animate things did not appear to populate the earth until the seventh period.

Other important possibilities are suggested by Genesis 1:11. These are the first reference to living things and may have a bearing on the problem of the origin of life and of its appearance on earth. The distinction made in the preceding sentence is intended to suggest that the origin of life is a problem separate and apart from the appearance of life on earth. Evidence is growing and is accepted by more and more scientists that life is widespread in the universe and hence need not have originated on the earth at all.

Consider the implications of the discovery and identification of complex molecules in space as introduced and discussed in connection with water in chapter 7. Investigators have been quick to realize that many space molecules are essential links between the simple chemical elements and living matter. Hydrogen cyanide (HCN) is involved in the proposed pre-life synthesis of amino acids and purines. Formaldehyde ($H_2C = O$), the prebiotic (prelife) precursor of glycine and the sugars, is common.

Fig. 17-1   The Great Nebula in Orion. This nebula is the site of discovery of many organic molecules and a place where life might be expected to appear.
(Palomar Observatory, California Institute of Technology.)

Cyanoacetylene (HC = C-CN) has been proposed as a precursor of the pyrimidines, cytosine and uracil. For some unknown reason there seem to be a strong tendency to form organic (carbon-based) molecules in space. Students of interstellar matter are convinced that the building up of organic compounds is going on in a continuous manner and on a widespread scale.

It is not surprising that the possibility of life arising and existing in interstellar space should be receiving serious attention. After all, if the essential elements are there along with an almost complete spectrum of radiant energy there appears to be no good reason why life might not arise just as easily in the clouds of space as in the environment of an earth-like planet. Any living thing small enough to float freely in the environment of an interstellar cloud would have a good chance of existing and even of reproducing indefinitely as long as favorable conditions continued. And there is no reason to suppose that a planet is any more or less permanent or long enduring than an interstellar cloud. Questions naturally arise as to just what level of complexity might be attained by floating life forms in space. Conditions would appear not to be unfavorable for large molecules, perhaps even cells, provided these could be individually in direct contact with the environment. It is likewise conceivable that such small entities might evolve to the point of being able to obtain energy by photosynthesis—the prerequisites for this basic process ought to be just as prevalent in certain interstellar clouds as they are on certain planets: Earth for example. Recent (1976) studies of the planet Jupiter have added other thoughts on extraterrestrial life. Jupiter has been described as a great "liquid drop" in allusion to the fact that most of it appears to be liquid hydrogen and other liquid components. One near-surface level or shell of the atmosphere consists of water vapor. It is seriously suggested that life could exist in this environment which certainly possesses a number of the basic requirements, such as water, a tolerable temperature, and energy sources of several sorts.

One of the most serious problems for photosynthetic organisms is that of maintaining their chloroplasts in the sunlight. They cannot operate in darkness, or under too much water, or in the

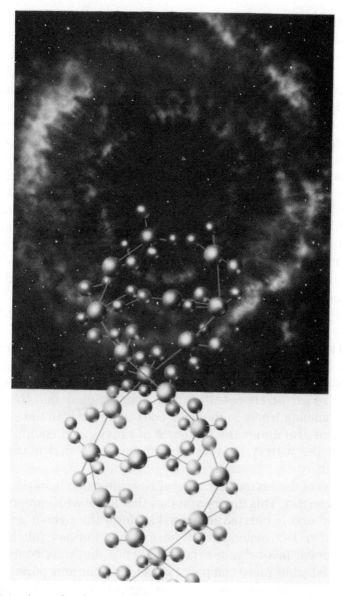

Fig. 17-2   A graphical representation of the thought that complex molecules, perhaps even living ones, may have originated in space. Like wandering spores such entities may have reached earth at a time when it was suited to propagate life.

(Hansen Planetarium, Salt Lake City, Utah.)

presence of strong radiation or in too much heat or cold. These are hinderances that earthbound plant life has adjusted to in various ways. It is possible to conceive situations in interstellar clouds in which many of these difficulties would be much less severe or even non-existent. Space is vast and conditions are varied. It is known that stars evolve from and appear in clouds of water-rich gas and dust. It seems safe to assume that whatever elements are in new stars must also have been in their ancestral clouds. If there are free-floating complex molecules of types that are basic to life it is only logical to assume that there are also traces of the minor elements that might be essential or at least helpful to the photosynthetic process. Likewise, considering the fact that clouds show varying degrees of opacity to radiation, it is probable that vast belts or zones are present that receive just the proper amount of energy for photosynthesis to operate. What a free-floating existence obviously does not provide is a solid base on which larger structures can grow. Surprisingly, evidence has been found that an earthly bacterium, *Serratia marcescens*, is able to live and reproduce in water vapor in the laboratory.

There are obvious limits to the advancement of life forms in space. Only through the organization of many-celled plants and animals is the ultimate potential of life realized. For these a solid earth-like surface is essential. This is not to deny that there are fish swimming freely in the open ocean and birds in the sky. But these are also under the influence of gravity and couldn't exist without the watery or atmospheric envelopes that accompany the earth.

One of the serious theories of how life came to earth is that of Panspermia. This theory assumes that life is widespread in the universe and is carried in spore-like form throughout space. If the proper key molecules or basic living entities fall into an environment favorable for their existence they may continue to evolve to higher more complex forms of life. Serious papers have been written on the possible "seeding" of the earth by comets. Thus life as we know it need not have originated on earth—it could well have arrived from an unknown place at a time when the earth was ready to receive it. The same "seeding" may have taken place on other planets but there, because of unfavorable conditions, life failed to survive. After all, this is the story of all airborne seeds and spores; a few take root, most do not. Thus it may be more accurate to speak of the *appearance* of life on earth than the *origin* of life on earth. Certainly the idea of Panspermia has much to recommend it especially in view of the discovery of complex molecules in space.

The meaning of this in the context of scriptural interpretation is that the origin of life, specifically, forms which can maintain themselves by radiant energy (plants in the broad sense), need not have been on earth or even in the near vicinity of the earth. All essentials for photosynthetic life forms can be supplied just as well if not better in interstellar space than they can in a

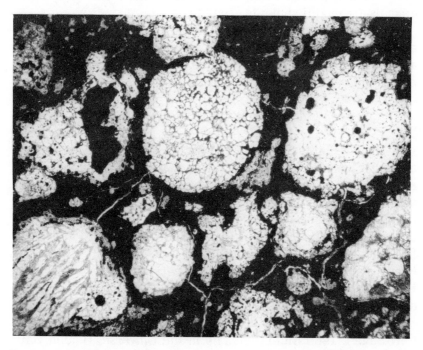

Fig. 17-3   Highly magnified cross-section of a meteorite of the carbonaceous chondrite class. The dark material is rich in carbon compounds and resembles asphalt. The round bodies are chondrules. These are so common in meteorites that many astronomers believe they may be the original building blocks of the solid bodies of the solar system.

(Courtesy Smithsonian Institution.)

planetary atmosphere or on a solid gravity-dominated surface. In the grand process of creation as hinted at in scriptures and discovered in more detail by modern science the appearance of light is a primary step and light is universal. Light-producing suns come and go as part of an evolutionary process.

Here also may be an explanation for the curious reference to plants in Genesis 2:5: "And every plant of the field before it was in the earth, and every herb of the field before it grew. . . ." Why are animals and man not included here? All life, not just plants, had a potential or spiritual existence before earth became a suitable habitation. Is this cryptic scripture a reminder that plants (in the broad sense) were actually in existence during the pre-earth period while animals were not? And in a sense animals are modified plants aren't they?

The seeming illogic of the Genesis story in having plant life appear before the creation of the sun may not be illogical after all. The Genesis order could well be essentially correct; another proof for a divine origin of the scriptures.

COMMENTS AND REFERENCES

The possibility that simple forms of life can originate, evolve, and exist in space is based on the known chemical and physical requirements for life as they are found on the earth. Any up-to-date encyclopedia article on botany describes the basic requirements of plant cells. A modern college textbook is Raven, Evert and Curtis, 1976, *Biology of Plants*, 2nd ed., Worth Publishers. Less technical and highly illustrated is F. W. Went, 1963, *The Plants*, a volume of the Life Nature Library, Time, Inc. The important interactions between plants and the atmosphere is described in James C. G. Walker, 1977, *Evolution of the Atmosphere*, Macmillan Publishing Co. A book by I. S. Shklovskii and Carl Sagan, 1966, *Intelligent Life in the Universe*, Holden Day, Inc., gives a broader perspective.

Several papers dealing specifically with the possibility of life in interstellar space or on other planets are found in Cyril Ponnamperuma, ed., 1976, *Chemical Evolution of the Giant Planets*. Subjects treated are life at low temperature, life in extreme environments, biological water requirements, and life on Jupiter.

Articles in popular scientific periodicals are: Barry E. Turner, 1973, Interstellar molecules: in *Scientific American*, March 1973; and R. M. Lemmon, 1976, Molecules of life: in *Astronomy*, vol. 4, no. 5; and Jupiter II: in *Science News*, July 17, 1976.

18

...EVENING AND MORNING
...THIRD DAY...

And the evening and morning were the third
day.

Genesis 1:13

During the third day a great number of significant happenings took place. According to Genesis the waters under the heavens were gathered together, the dry land emerged, and plant life was created. These three seemingly unrelated phenomena have already been briefly discussed. Looked at in cosmological terms the period we are dealing with is that between the creation of a galactic core and the appearance of well-developed spiral arms. Can all this be fitted into the framework of a single creative day in which a period or condition of darkness is followed by one of light?

Assume for purposes of building a coherent narrative that a condition of darkness, possibly a black hole, came into being at the center of the galaxy and was somehow necessary to the subsequent appearance of the glowing arms and spiral shape. If our hypothesis of the nature of the creative days is correct another period or state of light and a corresponding state of darkness must follow the black hole episode. Facts and speculations regarding the "gathering" of material and the emergence of a "dry" earth are in order. This event could not take place unless total conditions and associations were right. The birth of the earth was the outcome of ongoing events involving the sun, solar system and the galactic arm in which it lies. Consider first what a galactic arm is and what goes on in it in terms of the organization of matter.

The first impression one gets from looking at a spiral galaxy is that it is rotating like a spinning fireworks display or water going down a drain. Furthermore, since the arms are curved or coiled the rotation is clearly not that of a solid body such as a wheel with straight, rigid spokes. This impression is correct but the motion is not what one imagines on a common-sense basis. The system is truly turning but at a rate much faster than the arms themselves.

The explanation is based on what is known about the motions of the sun and earth. Our solar system is found to be

Fig. 18-1 A spiral galaxy viewed in such a way that the lighted spiral arms and intervening dark lanes are well shown.

(Courtesy Palomar Observatories, California Institute of Technology.)

moving around the center of the galaxy in an almost circular orbit on a journey that takes about 225-250 million earth-years to complete. This is the galactic year. Stars farther out than our sun take longer to complete their rotation; those nearer the center take shorter time. The hub or core of the galaxy seems to rotate as a solid body, like a rigid wheel as it were. A problem is immediately apparent. Since the earth is four and one-half billion years old it must have made at least sixteen journeys around the galaxy. But the evidence of galactic arms, including the Milky Way, is that they have made very few turns, generally only one or two. If they had made as many as the age of the solar system allows they would have been completely wound up to merge with the galactic center.

The explanation is that the spiral arms are only a pattern or configuration that is rotating much slower than the stars that make it visible. In purely physical terms an arm is a compressional wave that remains more or less stationary while matter passes into it, through it, and out of it. The stationary waves in a river are comparable. The waves are there in perfectly regular order but the water molecules that make up the crests and troughs are merely passing through them. Our solar system in its galactic year has passed into and out of the opposite spiral arms many times, right now it appears to be between two of them.

The wave theory explains why the arms are luminous and the lanes between are not. Basically, matter in the arms is being relatively compressed. The situation is comparable to that which creates sound waves in the atmosphere or earthquake waves in the earth. As the wave advances the transmitting material is alternately compressed and rarefied. Beyond calling attention to the probability of great explosive events in galactic centers we will ignore the problem of how waves may originate and spread in a system such as our galaxy. The visible effects are more important to the topic at hand.

In past chapters we have mentioned the effects of gravity in pulling material together to make the galaxies. This is a process that cannot operate unless certain areas become more dense or well supplied with matter than nearby areas. One effective way of creating unequal distributions of matter is a compressional or shock wave. In a galactic arm, it is supposed that matter is being compressed perhaps to ten times the density in regions behind and ahead of it. This is enough to initiate the formation of collapsing clouds and eventually stars. The theory agrees with what is observed—galactic arms are indeed sites of vigorous star formation. They glow from the abundance of new stars and also from the heating of adjacent clouds of dust and gas.

Vigorous chain reactions may be taking place in galactic arms. The condensations may be producing a certain number of larger than average stars that burn rapidly and are prone to run out their lives and explode into super novas. All this can happen while they are within a galactic arm. The violent shock waves passing through already compressed matter favors the creation of yet another family of stars including some that will take their turn as supernovas. This may account for the clotted patterns seen in the arms and for the fact that stars appear to be born in clusters or groups.

Currently (1980) the feeling among geologists and astronomers is that our solar system, sun, and planets originated as a result of a nearby supernova explosion. The visible effects of this creative event have faded away but some of the elements it produced were injected into the raw material of our system where they have been detected and dated.

Galaxies are obviously very dynamic objects. Matter flows within them and new and old stars pass out of the active arm regions into the intervening more peaceful dark lanes or bands. Stars do not fade or lose their lives between the arms. They shine on but the total aggregation is less luminous because dust and gas is not being energized to produce light and heat.

The subject of the third day may be summarized by pointing out the relations of light and darkness within what we call our galaxy. Attention naturally focuses on the lighted arms and the dramatic events that go on there. But consider the dark paths or lanes between the arms. These should not be thought of as empty space behind or beyond the glowing arms; neither are they devoid of matter or events. They are integral parts of the total patterns and are dark merely because matter within them is in a state of relative quiet and inaction.

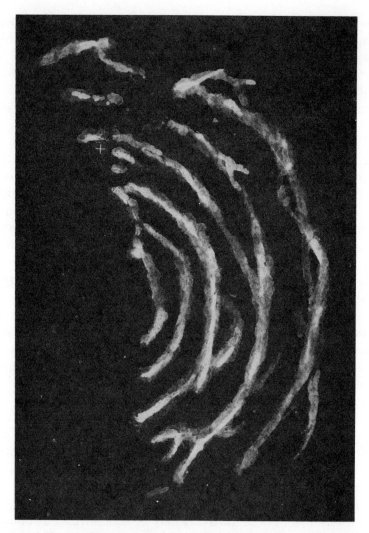

Fig. 18-2 The configuration of one half of the Milky Way galaxy as determined by earth-based radio receivers. What is shown is the intensity of radiation from hydrogen gas. The lighted lanes are thought to coincide with spiral arms such as are seen in other galaxies. The spaces between the lighted areas are on the order of 6,000 light years across and their configuration is indicative of how tightly the spiral arms are wound around the center. The location of the solar system is shown by a small cross near the outside of the half-section about two-thirds of the distance from the center. At some not too distant time the system has passed through one of the lighted areas. See text for a more complete explanation of galactic motions.

The pattern is not static. That which is in a lighted arm passes onward into the dark and that which is in the dark passes into and partakes of the light. The history of a star such as our sun illustrates the process. The first existence of our system was as part of a formless cloud in the dark band between the arms. Things changed as the slow rotation of the galaxy carried our potential solar system into the active glowing arm. There it was activated and became involved in the star-forming process. All that was needed was a degree of compression and gravity, strong enough to draw together the material of which sun and planets were to form. This initial "gathering" was certainly a rather sudden event. Production of the separate bodies within it also took place without delay. In a relatively short time a solid body called the earth appeared in the swirling mists.

Note that the birth of solar systems occurs in the transition from light to darkness—it is an event that takes place as darkness gives way to light. The process of dividing the light from the darkness is again a unique one. No matter how galactic arms are produced the events of the third creative day could not have been realities without the alterations of light and darkness that took place.

...TWO GREAT LIGHTS...
THE STARS ALSO

And God made *two great lights;* the greater
light to rule the day, and the lesser light to rule
the night: he made *the stars also.*

Genesis 1:16

The appearance of the sun and the moon, "two great lights"
set in the heavens to give light upon the earth is described as an
event of the fourth day. That these astronomical bodies should be
mentioned as appearing after the earth and even after the creation of plant life on the third day seems to contradict not only
common sense but also the basic facts of astronomy. But this is
not necessarily so. The emphasis of the scriptures is on the
function of the sun and the moon as light-givers rather than on
their formation as bodies in space. The wording of the scriptures
neither requires nor prohibits their initial creation on the third
day at the same time as the earth.

Students of scripture have speculated about this problem
and had reached logical conclusions a century ago. The key
thought in all arguments about the fourth day is that this was the
time at which the light of the sun, moon and stars first penetrated to the surface of the earth. I have a small book published
by J. H. Ward in 1884 titled *Gospel Philosophy Showing the
Absurdities of Infidelity and the Harmony of the Gospel with*

Science and Religion. In dealing with the events of the third and fourth periods the author of this precocious book remarks: "That ne sun and stars had been created long before this (the fourth day), we have no reason to doubt. We may, therefore correctly infer that they were then *for the first time visible from the surface of the earth.*" (p. 186, italics added.)

It is with regard to the nature of the material which prevented the penetration of light to the earth that a modern explanation must differ from that expressed in 1884. Earlier thinkers invisioned a shroud of watery clouds in the earth's atmosphere; today the obstructing material would be classified as dust and gas spread throughout the solar system. Any and all successful theories of the origin of the solar system start with a cloud of matter from which the sun, planets, satellites, comets and meteorites emerged. The gradual clumping together or gathering of material to make these separate solid bodies constitutes what is generally called the origin of the solar system or solar family. A late stage in the process was the clearing away of left-over remnants of dust and gas so that light could penetrate

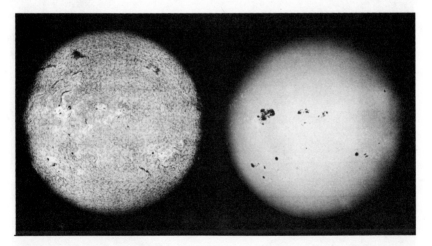

Fig. 19-1   Two photographs of the sun. The left view is taken by ordinary white light, the right view by red light produced by burning hydrogen. Note sun spots.

(Courtesy Palomar Observatories, California Institute of Technology.)

freely throughout the system. This relatively late stage of organization is entirely appropriate to the fourth period of the Genesis account.

Another topic deserves mention here. It is discussed as an explanation for those who might be inclined to retain the more literal view that the sun, moon and stars did not merely *appear* on the fourth day but that they actually did come into existence on that day.

Although Genesis describes the works of creation in a definite six-part sequence it is also clear that there could have been considerable overlap in the events that are described. As any storyteller knows there are difficulties in describing a series of simultaneous ongoing events taking place at separate localities. Of necessity the story follows a particular chain of events at one place to a certain point and then goes back to do the same for

Fig. 19-2   Full moon as seen from the earth. The moon does not always "rule the night"; it accompanies the sun in the daytime sky about half the time.
(Courtesy Palomar Observatories, California Institute of Technology.)

events at a second locality. In the terminology of the movies there are "flashbacks" or other devices to show relationships of overlapping or simultaneous events. The human mind can concentrate on only one subject at a time and the reader, or viewer even in imagination, can be in only one place at a time.

Thus Genesis describes mainly a series of separate consecutive events but there are also overlapping situations. Are we, for example, to suppose that the creation of the entire plant world was over and done with before the creation of any animals whatever? As plants and animals exist today they are essential to each other—plants provide food and oxygen for the consumption of animals while animals provide carbon dioxide for the photosynthesis of plants. Bees need flowers, flowers need bees. This is not to deny that in the history of the earth plants preceded

Fig. 19-3 Stars of the Pleiades cluster in the constellation Taurus. These stars are regarded as having formed at a relatively recent date perhaps within the last 50 million years.

(Courtesy Palomar Observatories, California Institute of Technology.)

animals and in their simple beginnings existed without benefit of animal life. Only later did their histories become interdependent and parallel.

A similar situation probably prevails in reference to the inanimate world of astronomical bodies. The record says: "And God made two great lights; the greater light to rule the day, and the lesser light to rule the night: he made the stars also." (Genesis 1:16.) If the order in which they are mentioned is to be strictly followed we must presume that the creation of the sun came first, then the moon, and finally the stars. Astronomers would scoff at the idea that the sun and the moon were produced before any of the stars. Common sense as well as the best scientific theory tells us that the phrase "he made the stars also" is not to

Fig. 19-4   Stars forming within a cloud of gas and dust. This photograph was obtained from x-rays by the High Energy Observatory that circles earth above the atmosphere.

(Courtesy NASA.)

Fig. 19-5   The immense numbers of stars in the galaxy may be visualized from this photograph of a region in the constellation Sagittarius. This view is toward the center of the galaxy and hence shows a maximum number of stars.

(Courtesy Palomar Observatories, California Institute of Technology.)

be understood as placing the creation of stars in any particular rigid position in the order of creation. After all there is good evidence that stars are forming at the present time. The statement about the stars was surely inserted to complete the record and what better place to include it than in a verse dealing with other astronomical matters? This guarantees that men should be informed that God did indeed create all things in heaven and earth.

We are frequently told that the ancients were great astronomers. While not disputing this it seems safe to say that little of a reliable or profound nature came down to today's scientists. What we know or think we know about astronomical matters has been won in historical time by slow degrees and by the labors of numerous identifiable individuals. It would seem that God left it up to man to discover by his own intellect how the stars were made. But let it be said that astronomers are the first to admit the incompleteness of their knowledge; much remains to be learned.

Accepting for the moment the thought that the creation account of Genesis is deliberately vague, incomplete, and cryptic but still basically true I take the position that it contains enough advanced information to prove that its source was the Creator himself. The task of full interpretation obviously lies in the future.

COMMENTS AND REFERENCES

The text of this chapter deals with the stars, the sun, and the moon, a subject matter so vast that an overwhelming amount of literature has been produced by those who are specialists in astronomy, astrogeology, cosmology and cosmogony. References are available at all levels of technicality. Those listed in connection with previous chapters should be consulted. Popular textbooks which treat the origin of stars are Stanley Wyatt, *Principles of Astronomy*, 2nd ed., 1971, Allyn and Bacon; Robert H. Baker and Laurence W. Fredrick, 1971, *Astronomy*, Von Nostrand Reinhold Co.; Thornton Page and L. W. Page (eds.), 1968, *The Evolution of Stars*, Macmillan; Lyman Spitzer and A. C. W. Cameron (eds.), 1966, *Stellar Evolution*, Plenum Press; Jay M.

Pasachoff, 1977, *Contemporary Astronomy*, Saunders. A good book on the solar system is William K. Hartmann, 1972, *Moons and Planets*, Bogden and Quigley; for data on the planets see Nicholas M. Short, 1975, *Planetary Geology*, Prentice-Hall; a popular book on the sun is George Gamow, 1964, *A Star Called the Sun*, Viking.

Encyclopedia articles on numerous astronomical topics are accessible in libraries. The popular magazine, *Astronomy*, is widely distributed, and astronomical events and discoveries appear in the news almost daily.

CHAPTER

20

...EVENING AND MORNING
...FOURTH DAY

And the evening and the morning were the fourth day.

Genesis 1:19

It is a common experience to see sunlight breaking through storm clouds to dispel darkness from the landscape. Ordinary earthbound clouds consist of condensed water vapor that is almost impervious to light. It is not difficult to imagine clouds thick and continuous enough to create total darkness. As air-travelers know the sun shines brightly above even the thickest cloud layer. Because interplanetary space is remarkably free of dust and gas very little light is lost in the ninety million miles between the sun and the earth's atmosphere.

According to prevailing theories the solar system began as a lightless cloud of dust and gas. Even after the central sun took form and began to send forth powerful radiation the surrounding cloud of dust and gas continued to shroud the planets in temporary but total darkness.

The agent responsible for clearing away the clouds of space and terminating the fourth period of darkness was the light and other radiation generated in the sun. This is called solar wind or radiation pressure and is a force that is known to exert measurable effects of many kinds. The best known and most spectacular manifestation of radiation pressure is the stream-lined appearance of the so-called "tails" of comets. Throughout most of their existence these relatively small bodies speed through the frigid depths of space in the form of frozen masses of stone and ice. When they sweep inward the heat of the sun vaporizes the more volatile constituents which break free as atoms or molecules to constitute the spectacular tails. A critical observation is that the material of a cometary tail always streams away from the sun. The tail does not stream behind like the exhaust of a rocket or the contrail of a high-flying aircraft. It is obvious that the solar wind, weak as it may be, in the absence of competing forces and in the near vacuum of space, is able to

Fig. 20-1 Artist's concept of an intermediate stage in the history of the solar system. The central sun, made luminous by thermonuclear reactions, is sending forth powerful radiation that is driving away lighter particles of gas and dust. Larger fragments called planetesimals will ultimately aggregate into presently existing members of the solar system.

(Painting by W.K. Hartmann, used with permission.)

drive small particles rapidly outward. The phenomenon of light pressure is demonstrated in every elementary physics laboratory by a device called a radiometer.

The energy output of the sun is thought to have been much greater during its youthful stages. New stars are always very brilliant. Stars of one class, called T Tauri stars, seem almost to be burning themselves to a premature death and may dispose of as much as 10 percent of their total mass before they settle down to a normal existence. Brilliance is an expression of radiation and the greater the brilliance of a star the stronger the radiation pressure on its surroundings. Although the stage of youthful vigor has passed, our sun is still driving particles of dust and gas out of the solar system.

There is something more. Because of gravitational attraction the original cloud of interplanetary dust and gas was prob-

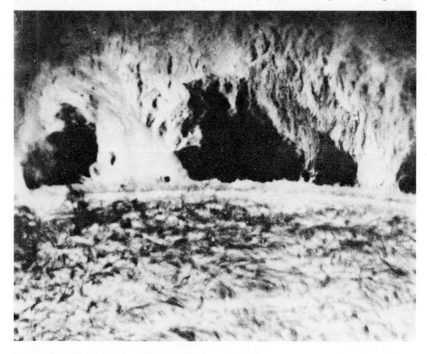

Fig. 20-2   The violent surface of the sun. Burning gas spouts and arches above the surface in prominences thousands of miles high.
(Courtesy Palomar Observatories, California Institute of Technology.)

ably denser in the vicinity of the planets then it was between them. Furthermore, it is logical to assume that the earth and moon once shared a common cloud that was thick enough to

Fig. 20-3 Sun and comet. This diagram illustrates the effects of the solar wind or light pressure on a comet as it swings into the inner parts of the solar system. At approximately the distance of Jupiter volatile components of the comet begin to vaporize and a tail appears. As the comet approaches the sun, more and more gas and dust are released and the tail blazes into prominence. The important fact is that the tail is always directed away from the sun, compelling evidence of the power of solar radiation in the emptiness of space.

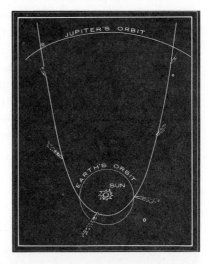

Fig. 20-4   Comet West, discovered in 1975. It has a very elongate orbit and its next return will be about one million years in the future.
(Lick Observatory Photograph.)

render either one invisible from the other. With the passage of time even this local cloud was cleared away so that not only the sun but also the moon became visible from the earth.

The dark phase of the fourth day was the period in which the sun was in existence but most of the solar system remained shrouded in an impenetrable cloud of dust and gas. The succeeding period of light began as the clouds cleared and sunlight penetrated to the earth for the first time. That the clearing process was effective and complete is indicated by the fact that not only the sun but also the moon and the stars appeared. Never since that time have the "lesser light" and the "greater light" ceased to rule the heavens of the earth.

21

... LET THE WATERS BRING FORTH ... THE MOVING CREATURE ... FIFTH DAY ...

> And God said, *Let the waters bring forth* abundantly *the moving creature* that hath life, and fowl that may fly above the earth in the open firmament of heaven.
>
> Genesis 1:20

The above text pertains to the appearance of animal life in the waters of the earth. The event is in its logical place in a sequence —first came plant life which may have appeared in interstellar space; second, animal life appeared in the waters of the earth on this, the fifth day, and later on the sixth day came land life. In distinguishing plants from animals the scriptures make use of the same basic characteristic by which science distinguishes them. Plants are immobile, animals are mobile. *A moving creature that hath life* is an excellent description of an animal as distinguished from a plant. (Readers with more technical knowledge will pardon lack of reference to plants that move such as slime molds, or animals that are fixed in place such as oysters.) Scriptural matters are of more immediate concern at this point.

The word "let" employed in Genesis has a number of meanings. In addition to introducing a command it might also request an opportunity or make a plea. Any of these three might be intended by the simple sentence: Let me go. Is the wording of

Fig. 21-1 This fanciful drawing that illustrates an **1885** edition of Milton's *Paradise Lost* shows some of the monstrous forms that the waters brought forth on the fifth day of creation. The whale, shown spouting in the distance, lends a small bit of realism to the scene. Flocks of birds flying above the surface are intended to emphasize the scriptural assertion that fowl too originated in the water.

Genesis intended to designate a commandment, an invitation, or an admonition? From Genesis a reader would almost surely be led to believe that the appearance of the different life forms was immediate with no delay and no lengthy preparations necessary. Reasons have already been given for believing that animal, like plant, life was yet to come to earth. Genesis 1 is merely describing the preparations.

The origin of life has always been a topic of great interest to man no matter what his stage of development and civilization has been. Primitive explanations exist in numerous myths and legends. These almost always contain magical and supernatural elements and are of obvious human origin. The idea of spontaneous generation by natural means is basic to any discussion of the origin of life. Many common observations justify a belief that higher animals can come from lower ones—thus caterpillars do become butterflies and tadpoles do become frogs. And it was not too difficult to believe that inanimate matter gives rise to complex living things. Flies are seen to crawl from dung heaps and mice skurry out of piles of old rags without obvious outside parentage. The belief that living things might thus originate from dead matter or lower beings was held by the learned as well as the common man during ancient and medieval times. Support for the theory of spontaneous generation also comes naturally from a literal reading of the scriptures. After all, the Bible plainly asserts that earth and water have the power to bring forth plants and animals as long as God permits it.

Spontaneous generation as it was understood in medieval times was discredited by the famous experiments of Louis Pasteur. His well-known demonstration was to expose one specimen of broth to ready access of airborne spores and an identical specimen to air but not to spores. As he confidently predicted the first specimen was contaminated, the second was not. Other experimenters went on to show that fly eggs are always necessary for the production of flies and that litters of young mice must always come from pregnant mother mice. Now no one believes that higher forms of life come spontaneously from nonliving matter.

Although Pasteur's experiments were hailed as a triumph for the experimental method they brought also a rather embarrassing and unexpected threat to science. If life cannot come by spontaneous generation how did it come in the first place? Obviously there is only one alternative—special creation. Since scientists are generally unwilling to accept a supernatural alternative they have had to admit the possibility that life has arisen, at least once, by spontaneous generation. The opinions of many if not most of those who are working in the field of biogenesis, which has to do with the origin of life, is that life could have arisen in a spontaneous manner *when conditions were right.*

That conditions must have been right at least once cannot be denied by either an atheistic scientist or a fundamentalist theologian. The scientist believes that life came by a spontaneous process and has been able to exist and progress on available resources over billions of years of time. The theologian believes that God acted upon the available materials of the earth which were ample and sufficient to support life thereafter for an apparently infinite period. God may have made earth out of nothing but living things were made of dust. And God considered his creations to be good and so pronounced them.

The inescapable conclusion is that *it is the organization of the elements and not their original production that is important.* This same basic truth was evident in previous steps of creation, particularly with regard to the earth as a planet. And what does organization mean? It means to arrange, to form, or to assemble simpler things into more complex things. Organization is God's method of creation.

The coming forth of living things did not follow immediately the gathering together, preparation, or organization of the elements. Conditions were not yet propitious for organic beings. They could only become favorable with the watering of the earth at the beginning of the seventh day.

Leaving aside the actual appearance of life, which for purposes of argument may be regarded as an entirely natural, indeed, inevitable product of the right organization of things, we can profitably consider what it is that must precede the event

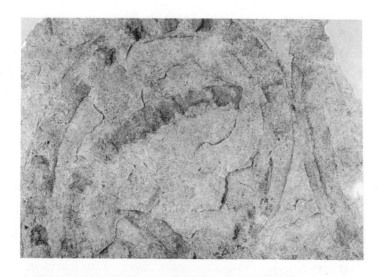

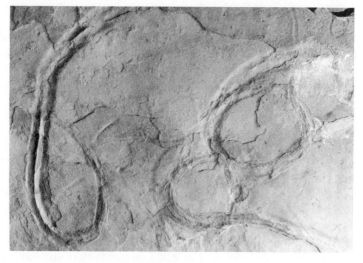

Fig. 21-2 Worm tracks in solidified sediment of Cambrian age estimated at almost a half-billion years old. Traces such as this constitute the earliest known evidence of animal life. They appear in marine rocks much older than hard-bodied animals such as trilobites. Makers of fossil "worm tracks" were soft-bodied and cannot be specifically identified. It is clear that most of them possessed a head with sense organs, well-developed digestive systems, and effective means of locomotion. They were, in other words, quite highly developed organisms. Distance across these specimens is about 7 inches.
(Courtesy T.S. Podrebarac.)

itself. Scientifically speaking, Earth became qualified as an abode of life not by a last-minute accident or miraculous re-organization of a barren planet but through a lengthy series of events which we are only now beginning to understand. Since the earth is our only actual example of a habitable planet its pre-life history is of paramount importance in any theory of creation. A brief tabulation of the prerequisites for life as we know it is appropriate:

1. Essential elements: All earth life requires certain chemical elements. These enter into the composition of all protoplasm no matter whether it makes up the simplest bacterium or a human brain. Hydrogen, carbon, nitrogen, oxygen, phosphorus and sulfur make up at least 95 percent of all protoplasm, and other prominent constituents are potassium, sodium, magnesium, calcium and chlorine. Most organisms also require traces of iron, copper, zinc, manganese, molybdenum, boron, fluorine, silicon, iodine and other elements.

All these elements must be and in fact are widely distributed everywhere on earth so as to be available to living things in all environments. It is not enough that the essential elements be present on the surface of the planet; all those mentioned are present on the Moon and probably on Mars but they are fixed in unbreakable combinations or are otherwise unavailable to life.

2. Water: Protoplasm is 80% water. Hydrogen and oxygen, the components of water, may be present in rocks and minerals but there must be a great excess of these elements for the production of the vast quantities of water such as exist on earth. Water is the great universal solvent and the agent which transports and distributes the other essential elements throughout the earth. This it accomplishes in running streams, in slowly percolating films in the soil, and in great currents that stir the entire ocean.

A little thought will convince anyone that other means of accomplishing the essential fluxing of elements exist on the planet Earth. Glaciers remove, grind up, mix, and redeposit sediment. Volcanic eruptions spew out pulverized dust from diverse subterranean sources to create temporarily lifeless but potentially fertile beds of ash. The wind picks up and carries dust particles everywhere; when these settle they constitute the most fertile soils on earth. Large sectors of Europe, China, and North America were blanketed by wind-blown soil (loess) during the Ice Age and now support a large fraction of mankind.

The slow-moving currents of the so-called "solid" earth accomplish the greatest mixing of all. Material from the ocean basins slowly moves toward great downsinking belts where it is melted and assimulated. Much of the melted material rises to the surface again to become part of the continents. What was formerly thought to be lost forever to the oceans is now known to return, even though very slowly, to build up the land.

3.   Suitable temperature: Evidences of water action throughout most of the geologic rock record is direct proof that the temperature has remained tolerable for immense periods of time. The temperature span between the freezing and boiling points of water (0-100° C) is almost by definition the range in which life can exist. Protoplasm must die if these limits are exceeded for any great length of time. Considering the great range of temperatures that exist in the universe it must be counted as providential, fortunate, or extremely unusual that the surface of the earth has remained within a very narrow temperature range. Not only was the temperature favorable for life to originate it has also remained within tolerable even comfortable limits ever since.

These brief comments suggest basic ways in which water takes part in life-supporting processes. Other roles of water in pre-life creative events have been mentioned in chapters 7 and 13. The wording used in the opening quotations of this chapter might be interpreted in two ways. Either water itself might be produced or previously existing water might be provided with the proper environment in which it could fulfill its intended role. The last interpretation seems preferable. Water may exist in clouds of space, in the depth of the earth or in ice or steam or vapor on the surface but it would not be suitable in these forms for supporting advanced animal life. The final preparation of water, mentioned as an event of the fifth day, comes when the earth itself is so organized and situated with regard to the central sun that water can exist and circulate in liquid and gaseous form.

The hydrological cycle is one of the marvels of the earth's physical systems. For it to operate there must be a large liquid

Fig. 21-3   Most commonly fossilized marine animals of early seas are the trilobites. These well-preserved specimens from Cambrian rocks of Alberta, Canada, are estimated as being about 550 million years old. Trilobites left no descendants and are only distantly related to anything in modern oceans. (Courtesy V. J. Okulitch.)

reservoir in the form of oceans and seas from which water vapor may escape by evaporation. The atmospheric moisture must then be carried by air currents to localities where it is caused to condense and fall as snow or rain. On the earth it gathers by gravity into streams that flow downward to the general ocean. On its journey through the ocean and sky and across the land water comes in contact with all forms of life. Were it not for the environment provided by the earth, water could not carry out its essential role in supporting life as it is known on earth.

COMMENTS AND REFERENCES

The topic of this chapter is the appearance of animal life on earth and in its waters. Much has been written on the subject and the trend in this writing has been steadily away from the idea of supernatural, instantaneous origin and toward natural, gradual, and long-term processes devoid of supernatural manifestations. An excellent discussion of various explanations of the origin of life is Charles H. Long, 1963, *Alpha, the Myths of Creation*, George Brasiller. Some general references written in the scientific vein are H. F. Blum, 1968, *Times Arrow and Evolution*, 3rd ed., Princeton University Press; H. Calvin, 1969, *Chemical Evolution*, Oxford University Press; Stanley L. and L. E. Orgel, 1974, *The Origins of Life on Earth*, Prentice-Hall, Inc.; M. G. Rulten, 1971, *The Origin of Life by Natural Causes*, Elsevier; S. W. Fox (ed.), 1965, *The Origin of Prebiological Systems*, Academic Press.

A semi-popular easily understandable book that is entirely evolutionary in approach is Ruth Moore and the Editors of Life, 1964, *Evolution*, Time, Inc. The entire September 1978 issue of *Scientific American* is devoted to the single topic of organic evolution. For anyone having only limited time this is perhaps the most factual and comprehensive reference available.

Anti-evolution literature may be obtained from the Institute for Creation Research (ICR), 2716 Madison Avenue, San Diego, California 92116. Titles available from this source include: Scientific Creationism; Evolution? The Fossils Say No!; The Genesis

Record; Bible Cosmology and Modern Science; The Bible and Modern Science, and many others. Over a period of many years the *Plain Truth* magazine issued by the Worldwide Church of God has carried many anti-evolution articles.

22

...EVENING AND MORNING ...FIFTH DAY

And the evening and the morning were the fifth day.

Genesis 1:23

The fifth division of light and darkness is restricted specifically to planet Earth. The basis for division is simple enough — the original dark earth melted and passed through a temporary molten light-giving stage. That this was an essential phase of earth history is almost universally accepted by geologists. Common-sense observations support the idea and non-scientists should not find it a difficult one. Anyone who has witnessed the violent expulsion of steam, smoke, and molten lava from volcanoes should have no trouble in believing that the interior of the earth is hot enought to be melted. This thought also fits well with early theories which derive the earth directly from the sun. The thinking is simple enough: since the earth commenced as a fragment of molten material torn from a molten sun it must now be in the process of cooling off. As everyone knows a heated object such as a baked potato cools from the outside inward. This phenomenon gave rise to the term "crust of the earth"; the term is graphic and true enough to hold its place in modern geologic terminology. We do live on the crust of the earth; it is the part we know the most about.

After decades of argument over whether the earth took form as a hot or a cold body the weight of evidence is judged to favor a cold or at least non-molten beginning. A problem emerges: how could an originally cold, solid body become hot enought to melt? As it turns out there is no lack of possible heat sources. The original thought was that the mere drawing together or compaction of the materials of the earth might raise its temperature to the melting point. This is certainly possible for larger bodies—we have seen how pressures within masses the

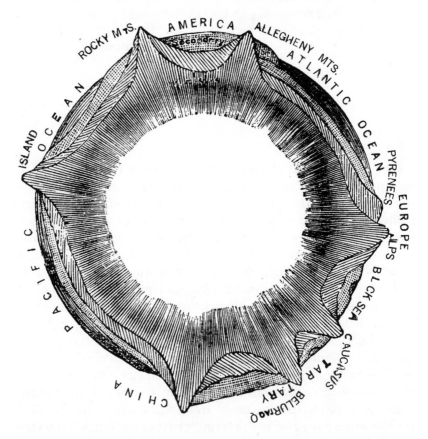

Fig. 22-1   Structure of the earth as it was visualized in the middle of the nineteenth century. The molten center is emphasized. Modern geophysics has revealed a more realistic concept but the core of the earth is still regarded as being molten. (See Figure 16.3 for comparison.)

size of the sun caused them to become self-luminous. Smaller objects such as Earth apparently cannot generate energy for nuclear reactions by compaction alone.

Enter radioactivity. This mysterious source of energy was discovered in 1896 and the most important radioactive element, uranium, was studied by Madam Curie. Other naturally occurring radioactive elements are thorium and potassium, the latter being relatively abundant. As uranium and thorium atoms convert to lead and potassium-40 becomes argon-40 a small but

Fig. 22-2 The molten earth as seen from the moon. The condition depicted here may have existed about four billion years ago. At this time, by a special combination of agencies the earth was totally melted and became temporarily a self-luminous body. At this same time the sun, shown on the left, was probably more luminous and powerful than it now is. By the combination of powerful solar radiation and its own self-generated heat the earth was stripped of all volatile materials that emerged from the interior at this time. In this view streams of gas are shown being driven into space by solar radiation. Later, as the earth cooled, most of the expelled material, including water, remained on the surface.

measurable amount of heat is released. Locked within the earth and blanketed by miles of overlying rock radioactive heat is thought to have reached a level sufficient to melt the earth or at least certain shells or zones within it.

Fig. 22-3   Surface of the Moon as photographed from earth.
(Photo courtesy Mount Wilson Observatories.)

One more potential heat source has only recently been conceived as a possible factor in melting the earth. This is the impact of large comet-like bodies or asteroids that invaded the solar system about 4 billion years ago. The reality of a gigantic bombardment is strongly emphasized by the discovery of great impact craters on Mercury, Mars, the Moon, and several rocky satellites of Jupiter and Saturn. The largest of these scars are the oldest—they are overlain and marred by smaller, younger craters. Evidence is that a swarm of gigantic bodies swept through the solar system to scar every solid body in their path.

It is presumed that Earth did not escape the general havoc. It was impacted but with different results. It is theorized that the infalling bodies penetrated deeply and created enough energy to trigger the melting of the entire globe. This on the assumption that the earth had already been heated to a significant degree by radioactivity and compaction. No matter how it came about the earth melted and the evidences of the earlier impacts were swallowed up. It is true that subsequent craters, some of them relatively large, were formed on earth but these have been mostly obliterated by erosion and other dynamic geologic processes. Meteor Crater in northern Arizona is our best-known example of a fairly recent impact.

Fig. 22-4 Glowing molten lava erupting from a Hawaiian volcano. The entire Hawaiian chain, including many submarine islands, has resulted from eruptions such as this. There is no evidence that prehistoric eruptions have been significantly larger than those observed in historic time. Basalt is the chief type of rock produced; and, if the ocean bottoms are considered, this is the most common type of material at the surface of the globe. In general the amount of lava expelled from the earth has been declining with time.

(Courtesy U. S. Geological Survey.)

Our final argument requires acceptance of methods of dating the age of the earth and of rocks. Many lines of evidence place the age of the earth at four and one-half billion years. Yet, in spite of intensive exploration no actual rocks over 3.7 billion years have been found. This is explained by geologists as a result of the complete melting and destruction of all older rocks at or near the time of the giant impacts. On the other hand rocks as old or older than the bombardment have been brought back from the moon. This body was not completely melted and so preserves rocks and even a landscape that goes back almost to the time of its formation.

The foregoing paragraphs offer explanations for belief that the earth was once molten. Many conditions seen on the earth and associated planets and satellites are compatible with if not actually dependent on this event. The consequence of importance to the topic of creative subdivisions is that the earth became luminous as it melted. Lava is incandescent and luminous as long as it is molten. At the time of melting the entire earth was encased in lava and was at least temporarily a light-producing body.

Thus by another unique combination of light and darkness the fifth day of creation was accomplished. A most important consequence of melting was the production of water and the potential for the life forms that cannot exist without it.

... BEAST OF THE EARTH ... CATTLE ... CREEPING THING ... MAN ... SIXTH DAY ...

And God said, Let the earth bring forth the living creature after his kind, cattle, and creeping thing, and beast of the earth after his kind: and it was so.

And God made the beast of the earth after his kind, and cattle after their kind, and every thing that creepeth upon the earth after his kind; and God saw that it was good.

And God said, Let us make man in our image, after our likeness: and let them have dominion over the fish of the sea, and over the fowl of the air, and over the cattle, and over all the earth, and over every creeping thing that creepeth upon earth.

So God created man in his own image, in the image of God created he him; male and female created he them.

And God blessed them, and God said unto them, Be fruitful, and multiply, and replenish the earth, and subdue it: and have dominion over the fish of the sea, and over the fowl of the air, and over every living thing that moveth upon the earth.

And God said, Behold, I have given you every herb bearing seed, which is upon the face of all the earth, and every tree, in the which is the fruit of a tree yielding seed; to you it shall be for meat.

And to every beast of the earth, and to every fowl of the air, and to every thing that creepeth upon the earth, wherein there is life, I have given every green herb for meat: and it was so.

And God, saw every thing that he had made, and, behold, it was very good. And the evening and the morning were the sixth day.

Genesis 1:24-31

A great deal of information is contained in the eight verses that describe the events of the sixth day. This is understandable as it was during this period that higher forms of animal life and man himself became possibilities. The first two verses pertain to all land-living animals. "Creeping things" no doubt designates most insects, the less common crawling or walking invertebrates such as snails and even many reptiles and amphibians. "Cattle" and "beasts of the field" would seem to comprise both wild and domestic mammals. The Bible follows the same sequence as geology and biology textbooks which recognize an age of sea life followed by an age of land life. According to the findings of those who study ancient life the age of animal land life began with the emergence of air-breathing invertebrates and vertebrates in the Devonian Period about 400 million years ago. By then plants were already established on land but had not been there for long. It is one of the mysteries of the history of life that colonization of the lands was so long delayed. A believable explanation is that exposure to the full power of sunlight is dangerous and deadly and would have been fatal until atmospheric oxygen had accumulated in sufficient quantity to constitute the ozone layer that now forms a protective shield around the globe. It seems ironical that earth's highest creature, man, now has the power to destroy the ozone layer and in fact may be doing so.

Three verses of the sixth-day description are devoted to the subject of man, stressing the points that he was created in the image of the Gods, that both male and female appeared, that mankind should be fruitful in multiplying and replenishing himself, that he should subdue the earth, and finally that he should have dominion over all other living things. The instruction to multiply and replenish, to take dominion over other species and to subdue the earth seems to have been followed by mankind to an ultimate extreme, even to a fault as it were. The twin problems of overpopulation and depletion of resources are now man-

Fig. 23-1   God creating animal life from the ground by his direct command. This old print unmistakably expresses the creationist view that the species appeared in perfect, unchanging form in a sudden and miraculous manner.

kind's chief concern. Has man become too fruitful? Has he subdued the earth too thoroughly, perhaps to the point of harming it in incurable ways? These are problems that go far beyond the scope of this book and in spite of their importance cannot be considered further here.

Two verses out of eight are devoted to what are plainly dietary matters. Basic is the assertion that all animal land life (including fowls) are to seek and find their food supply in the vegetable world. This appears to be self-evident today. Significantly, the word green is used in describing plants that are intended for food. Science might translate this into a reference to photosynthesis which is the basic food (energy) producing process for all life, both plant and animal. Since the directive is clear that the "meat" of man should be from herbs and trees one might ponder the thought that by well-managed vegetarianism the food shortages and dietary ills of the world might be alleviated.

It is easy to forget in reading Genesis that the creations of the sixth day, namely animal land life and man are not to appear as actual beings until the seventh day. It was the physical preparations that took place on the sixth day. Since the preparations

Fig. 23-2   These regularly spaced impressions are regarded as the oldest evidence of land-living, four-footed animals. The rock slab on which they are preserved was discovered in rocks of the Devonian period, estimated at 375 million years old, in Australia. The specimen is about 3½ feet long.
(Courtesy Norman A. Wakefield.)

for sea life had been completed on the fifth day there must have been something significantly different having to do with land life that was not yet accomplished on the pre-life earth during the fifth day. And if our analysis is right both preparations for sea life and the preparations for land life took place before it rained on the earth. How can these constraints be satisfied?

A possible sequence of events is strongly suggested by recent scientific discoveries but the details will undoubtedly need refinement. According to the best current theory the waters of the earth came out of the interior as it cooled from a molten condition or solidified to a compact state. The capacity to produce water must be counted as the most obviously essential attribute of a planet intended to support seas and oceans. Yet, the capacity to produce water or even its actual production is not necessarily equivalent to the filling of the oceans or even the production of rain. What is found on Mars supports this statement. Mars has water but there are neither oceans nor life as far as we can tell.

There was probably a stage in the history of the planet when all liquid or gaseous materials, including water that reached the surface, were swept away as soon as they appeared. An entirely effective mechanism for doing this exists in the radiation pressure from the sun (solar wind) that was probably much stronger at that early time. In other words the earth had already "come up dry" and was capable of producing water but the accumulation of water bodies on its surface was for a time prevented by external forces. (See Figure 22-2.)

What is there in the above situation that is unfavorable to the ultimate appearance of land life? An answer is obvious; there are no provisions for land or more specifically for continents. One can easily imagine a globe entirely flooded by water. On the face of it this should be the structure of the earth—first, a sphere of solid material, then a layer of water, and finally an atmosphere, all these being in successive layers according to density. As far as we know the interior of the earth is a succession of shells neatly constructed of nested spheres surrounding a heavy central core. The gaseous envelope is likewise composed of a half-dozen world-circling "spheres" ranging from heavier to lighter outward. Only the water or hydrosphere breaks the neat expectable pattern. The water of the earth is not in a continuous layer even though it might well be. There is enough water to form an unbroken world-circling ocean 8,000 feet deep. But it is the continents that break up the continuity of the water, not the water that breaks up the continuity of the land.

Why continents? Why is the lighter material of the earth's crust piled up in irregular pancake-like patches rather than being in a uniform layer as might be expected? The problem looms even larger when it is realized that erosion by water, wind and ice is continually at work to wear down the land. The fact is that continents have been in existence for a very long time, several billion years according to geologic reckoning, and yet they seem to be just as large and high as they ever were.

In spite of their present prominence and apparent durability there must have been a time when there were no continents, and even more important, no mechanism for creating and maintaining them. When the earth was molten and for a while thereafter the surface material of the globe was probably quite uniformly distributed. There were no elevated land masses that could become continents or basins to contain oceans when water became available.

How continents were made and are maintained has now been explained by a very satisfactory theory. The process goes by the name of sea-floor spreading. Space again prohibits a complete discussion but there are many good non-technical explanations (see references). Briefly the process is this: From a great system of world-circling submarine mountains that more or less bisect the great ocean basins lava is emerging from within the earth on a grand scale. This material does not pile up, it rises and fills an everwidening rift or great crack as the sides move apart. It is not understood why this rift system continues to open, but it clearly has been doing so for an immense period of time. Earthquakes and volcanoes accompany the general unrest. The most amazing fact about the process is that the material thus created is carried away or pushed aside to become part of the ocean bottom. In time any strip of once-liquid lava is displaced tens, hundreds and even thousands of miles away from its original position. This is what is called sea-floor spreading. The ocean basins are splitting apart.

But it is obvious that the sea bottoms cannot expand indefinitely without encountering a continent or another section of ocean bottom. It doesn't help to know that some continents are carried or pushed along by the expanding process; even these must eventually collide with other sections—the space on the earth's surface is constant. The great moving plates, some with continents, some without, do inevitably collide and it is what happens along the colliding fronts that neatly explains how the process works and what causes continents. When two plates push together one usually is forced downward and is overridden by the other. South America, for example, is pushing over the Pacific plate, the ascending plate is being forcibly elevated into the Andes chain. The descending plate does not remain intact

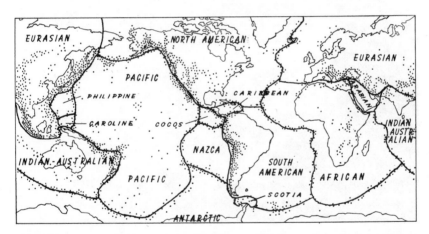

Fig. 23-3 The major rocky plates of the outer brittle shell of the earth. Each plate is reacting independently by moving away from and colliding with its neighbors. As plates move slowly apart (as in the mid-Atlantic) the resulting rift is filled with lava that rises from below; where the plates push together mountains are raised and there is heightened volcanic and earthquake activity (as along the western coast of South America); where sliding motions occur there is intense earthquake activity (as along the San Andreas fault system in California). The great system of related and interlocking movement is called plate tectonics. [Adapted from William Lee Stokes, Sheldon Judson, and M. Dane Picard, Introduction to Geology (Englewood Cliffs, N.J.: Prentice-Hall, 1978), p. 35.]

and inert—almost at once it begins to melt and soon is consumed into the heated plastic layer below. The material of which a descending plate is composed thus becomes part of the world-

Fig. 23-4 Where continents touch. Historic lands and water bodies shown in this view from space include the southeastern Mediterranean Sea on the left; the vegetated Nile Delta in the foreground with the Suez Canal truncating its upper corner; the Gulf of Suez in the upper middle right; a small section of the Red Sea, extreme upper right; the barren Sinai Peninsula, upper center; the narrow Gulf of Aqaba parallel with the upper margin; and the Dead Sea faintly visible near the left edge. The linear depression that cradles the Dead Sea and the Gulf of Aqaba is a continuation of the Dead Sea rift and a very important junction of the earth's moving plates. Human history has been profoundly influenced by the geologic activity of this region. (NASA.)

circling reservoir below and can be extruded again at the mid-ocean ridges to complete the cycle.

Very important to note is that when ocean meets continent it is the oceanic plates that are forced downward; they are heavier and lower to begin with. However, a great deal of lighter material from these plates is literally scraped off against the continents to make them wider and even higher. Also, once a plate melts its lighter constituents tend to rise and break forth in volcanoes adding still more material to the lands. This is the origin of the volcanic ring-of-fire around the Pacific ocean. That these volcanoes are busily making new islands and adding to older lands is a matter of observation.

The whole concept of splitting volcanic mountains, spreading sea floors, colliding continents and recycling of earth materials generally is conveyed by the term plate tectonics, or global tectonics. It is a view of things that has revolutionized earth science on a par with the Copernican revolution in astronomy and the Darwinian revolution in biology. Its importance to our present subject is that the beginning of the land (continent) building process must have happened in the distant past after the cooling of the interior of the earth but before the appearance of fossils. Geologists are agreed that the process of plate tectonics is a phenomenon that would be expected in a cooling layered planet such as earth. That no other planet of the solar system has been thus affected or has the proper structure and internal composition to be affected is now evident. Earth becomes more unusual with each space mission.

In the context of scriptural interpretations the preparation of earth (land) to bring forth or support air-breathing animal life was the work of the sixth creative period. Mechanisms had to be set up that would permit land life to emerge when conditions were right. Such a land-creating and land-maintaining mechanism is now evident and it became operative at the right time in the scriptural creation sequence.

COMMENTS AND REFERENCES

One of the last stages in the preparation of the earth was

156

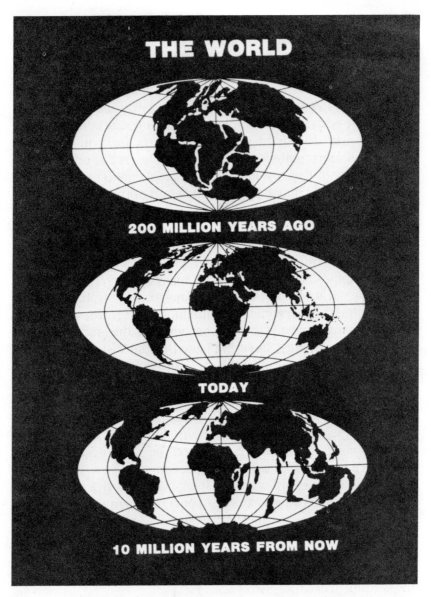

Fig. 23-5 The major geographic features of the earth as they were, as they now are, and as they may become in the distant future. The theory of plate tectonics provides an acceptable explanation not only for the origin of continents but also for many major changes of the prehistoric past.
(NASA.)

the appearance of land areas suitable for the air-breathing animals that were destined to appear. The process by which continents and islands are created has been discovered and is known by the scientific name of plate tectonics. The subject has received wide publicity and since about 1970 has been integrated into textbooks at all levels. The following general geology books are recommended: W. L. Stokes, Sheldon Judson, and M. D. Picard, 1978, *Introduction to Geology*, Prentice-Hall; L. Don Leet, Sheldon Judson, and M. E. Kauffman, 1978, *Physical Geology*, Prentice-Hall; Frank Press and Raymond Siever, 1974, *Earth*, Freeman.

Books dealing specifically with the subject of the development of the earth's major features as explained by plate tectonics are: A. A. Hallam, 1971, *A Revolution in Earth Sciences: From Continental Drift to Plate Tectonics*, Oxford University Press; Ursula B. Marvin, 1973, *Continental Drift: The Evolution of a Concept*, Smithsonian Institution Press; Walter Sullivan, 1974, *Continents in Motion: The New Earth Debate*, McGraw-Hill. A collection of excellent papers from the *Scientific American* is J. Tuzo Wilson (ed.), 1972, "Continents Adrift," Freeman. A follow-up selection from the same source is "Continents Adrift and Continents Aground," 1976.

The *National Geographic* magazine has published two excellent articles: Samuel W. Matthews, "This Changing Earth," Jan. 1973; and J. R. Steirtzler and Emery Kristof, "Project Famous," May 1975. Articles in other popular magazines are Tom Alexander, "A revolution called plate tectonics has given us a whole new earth," *Smithsonian*, Jan. 1975; Dan R. McKenzie, "Plate tectonics and sea-floor spreading," *American Scientist*, July-August 1972.

... AFTER HIS KIND

And God said, Let the earth bring forth grass, the herb yielding seed, and the fruit tree yielding fruit *after his kind*. . . .

And the earth brought forth grass . . . herb . . . tree . . . *after his kind:* and God saw that it was good. . . .

And God created great whales, and every living creature that moveth, which the waters brought forth abundantly, *after their kind*, and every winged fowl *after his kind*. . . .

And God said let the earth bring forth the living creature *after his kind*, cattle, and creeping thing, and beast of the earth *after his kind*. . . .

And God made the beast of the earth *after his kind*, and cattle *after their kind*, and every thing that creepeth upon the earth *after his kind*.

Genesis 1:11-25

So far as plants and animals are concerned Genesis 1:11-25 are critical scriptures. Some of the important concepts they contain have already been discussed. What is to be emphasized here are those scattered passages that illustrate usage of the phrases *after his kind* and *after their kind*.

It is often said that the scriptures explain themselves. A problem raised by one verse may often be explained by a verse somewhere else. This is the reason men search, and do not merely read, the scriptures. Certain it is that only by cross-reference and comparison can a student be sure that he has at least looked at all the evidence. There are thirty occurrences of the phrase "after his kind" in the Bible. Nine of these are in the first chapter of Genesis, three are in Genesis 6, four in Genesis 7, one in Genesis 8, nine in Leviticus 11, and four in Deuteronomy 14. Here then is an unusual abundance of comparative usages.

As the phrase in question appears in Genesis 6, 7 and 8 it has to do with the Flood and Noah's Ark in particular. Noah was instructed as follows:

> And of every living thing of all flesh, two of every sort shalt thou bring into the ark, to keep them alive with thee; they shall be male and female.

Fig. 24-1 Animals enter the Ark as Noah receives communication from God. This illustration is from a Luther Bible of 1564. Animals entering the Ark were described as ". . . every beast after his kind, and all the cattle after their kind, and every creeping thing . . . after his kind . . . every fowl after his kind, every bird of every sort." (Genesis 7:14.) That this is the same terminology used in the creation scriptures would seem to allow more than one meaning to the phrase "after his kind."

> Of fowls after their kind, and of cattle after their kind, of every
> creeping thing of the earth after his kind, two of every sort shall
> come unto thee, to keep them alive.
>
> Genesis 6:19-20

The animals that entered the ark when the rains came are
described:

> . . . and every beast after his kind, and all the cattle after their
> kind, and every creeping thing . . . after his kind . . . every fowl
> after his kind, every bird of every sort."
> And they went in unto Noah into the ark two and two of all
> flesh. . . ."
>
> Genesis 7:14-15

At a later date in Hebrew history it again became necessary
to deal with large groupings of animals in relation to their use as
food. In Leviticus 11 instructions are given as to "what may
be eaten and what may not, of beast, of fishes and of fowls." The
following verses are pertinent here:

> And the vulture and the kite after his kind;
> Every raven after his kind;
> And the owl, and the nighthawk, and the cuckoo, and the hawk
> after his kind, . . .
> And the stork, the heron after her kind, and the lapwing, and
> the bat. . . .
> Even these of them ye may eat; the locust after his kind, and
> the beetle after his kind, and the grasshopper after his kind.

What do these usages of "after his kind" have in common?
In the creation episode the phrase occurs in connection with the
bringing forth of living things, especially as these are mentioned
in certain natural groupings such as grass, herbs, trees, moving
creatures, winged fowl, cattle, etc. In the flood story the usage is
in connection with the creatures Noah was to bring into the Ark,
again in certain groupings such as fowl, cattle, beasts of the
field, and creeping things. Finally in the dietary instructions of
Leviticus the term "after his kind" again designates certain related species that are not to be eaten. It is not to be wondered at
that since there are more birds than there are mammals greater
detail as to what is to be eaten had to be given. Although the

Leviticus listing becomes quite specific it still does not name all the species—what is named are genera or families instead.

All scriptural uses of "after his kind" appear when there is a necessity to classify, enumerate, or designate by groups a large number of species. This is reasonable. When the need to name a great number of related things involves dozens, hundreds or thousands of names one must consolidate and abbreviate. There are many devices such as using et cetera (the familiar etc.) In a textbook giving the basic classification of plants and animals I find it convenient to name one or two common examples and the rest by inference under the term "kin"; thus, oysters and kin, starfish and kin, mushrooms and kin. Obviously this device is a great time and space saver in writing and thinking. On the other hand it leaves much to the imagination and much room for un-certainty and dispute. A precise and complete classification or enumeration would require a lengthy list with everything in its place. The reminder that about 2 million living things have already been named indicates the scope of the problem.

The whole subject of what is intended by use of the word "kind" in the creation scripture might be dropped at this point with the conclusion that it is merely a convenient phrase like etc., "and kin," or "such like." Perfectly good sense can be made of phraseology such as "cattle and such like," "beasts of the earth and such like," and "the owl . . . and his kin," or "the raven and such like."

To drop the subject here, however, leaves too many things unanswered. Even though the intent of scripture was to present an inclusive classification in shortened form, this has evidently not been the message received by most readers. The idea that "after his kind" has to do with reproduction seems to dominate most interpretations of Genesis 1 and 2. "After his kind" is com-monly taken to mean that each originally created plant or animal "kind" must reproduce unchanged and unchanging until the end of its existence. That which was created as an amoeba can never be anything but an amoeba, a worm nothing but a worm, a monkey nothing but a monkey. This concept has received the designation of the "fixity of species" and is a cornerstone of anti-evolutionary or Creationist belief. Obviously the idea that one kind of organism is prohibited by divine decree from giving rise to another kind needs to be examined in connection with the subject matter of this chapter.

WHAT IS A KIND?

One of the marks of a good language is that it contains words that are specific and words that are general. Thus English provides the word *species* that is specific and the word kind that is general. It is fortunate that the word kind has not been given a specific meaning and is still open to use in the common vernacular. Furthermore, kind has served a general function ever since it was used in early biblical translations. The first use of the word species in a technical sense was in the mid-16th century but other categories of the present system of biological nomenclature were not used formally until later. In the mid-18th century the "great namer," Carl von Linne (Linnaeus) brought out a system with six levels: kingdom, class, order, genus, species, and variety. This means that in the earlier translations of the Bible the word kind could have had only a very general meaning and only subsequently could it possibly be equated with anything scientific at all.

Everyone knows that there are many distinct kinds of living things. A scientist might substitute the word species for kinds in the above sentence; but if he does he is using a technical term and should be expected to define it. At first this seems easy enough — things that look alike are the same species. But it is not this simple. Several hundred years of study and observation have seemingly made the problem of defining a species more difficult. Appearances are deceptive; many cases are known of two perfectly good species, each able to reproduce within its own group but not with the other, and yet no visible differences between the two. The name cryptic species applies where visible differences cannot be detected.

Perhaps the most widely held definition of species hinges on the matter of whether or not individuals under consideration can successfully interbreed. Thus a species is *a group of similar individuals which can interbreed and produce offspring that are in turn fertile with each other.* This is a practical definition but it does not take into account the great number of hybrids that are known, particularly among plants. Some hybrids exist for long time periods and are distinct from the parents that produced

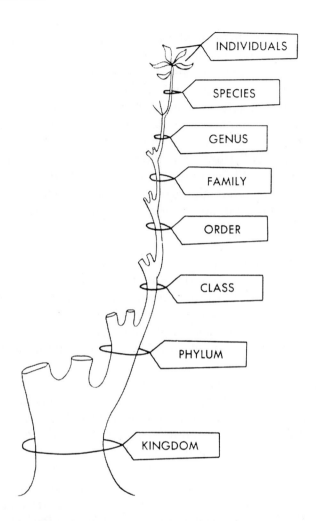

Fig. 24-2 The different major categories or levels of classification as currently used by biologists. Each individual plant or animal, as represented by a leaf, is a member of a certain species, which is in turn a division within a higher group, the genus, and so on. Some branches have more subdivisions than others; for example, the order of rodents is more numerous than the order of carnivores. A man is not only a member of man "kind" but also of all the other groups up to and including animal "kind." Which of the many branches of the diagram is the scriptural kind? From William Lee Stokes, *Essentials of Earth History*, 1st edition (Englewood Cliffs, New Jersey: Prentice-Hall, Inc., 1960), p. 122.

them. How much hybridization is permissible between parent species for these parents to be considered separate species?

Consider extinct species. Those who study fossils cannot apply the test of reproduction. What is left for study are dead and mainly incomplete specimens. To the paleontologist a species must be an identifiable group that persists through time without fusing with some other group. This is a highly theoretical definition; but it does call attention to the fact that species not only exist as living things but have a history in the past that must be taken into account. The great edifice of life is not a one-story building.

In a facetious but still serious way someone has said that a species is something that a reliable specialist has recently said is a species.

Anti-evolutionists have placed a great deal of emphasis on the crossing of animals and plants one with another. They take the phrase "after his kind" to mean that nothing that can cross with something else is a distinct kind. Since many species do cross, particularly among plants and lower animals, the anti-evolutionists are reluctant to accept species as equivalent to kinds. Even genera (next highest category above species) also cross and are thus eliminated as being scriptural kinds. So one must go to a higher category still. It is at the family level where everyone feels fairly safe that there is no crossing. Consequently, anti-evolutionists have taken a fairly strong stand that the biologist's family is the scriptural kind.

The endless and largely fruitless entanglements with the meaning of words that is illustrated in the above paragraphs should convince almost anyone of the absurdity of trying to place a restrictive technical meaning on what was intended to be a general term. All difficulties are swept away if we accept a definition of kind as being anything that reproduces successfully. A kind might then be a species, a genus, a family or even something broader. It might also be something less than a species such as a variety or a race; even hybrids would not be excluded. A kind could be a simple sexless bacteria, an organism with alternations of generations, a plant that propagates by branching or budding, and so upward to those higher things which produce fertilized eggs and living young.

WHAT ABOUT FOSSILS?

In seeking ways to prove the literal truth of the scriptures creationists have found what they consider to be a great and fatal weakness in the evolutionist argument. Their point of attack is the imperfection of the fossil record of past life. The argument is this: evolution teaches that all species must be derived from previous species but the fossil record fails to supply the necessary stages in the postulated family trees.

According to strict creationism only divine intervention can produce the original kinds of plants and animals. Evolutionists believe that all levels of living things are produced by naturally occurring changes in the genes. The argument can be simplified to the question of the reality of the so-called "missing links." Creationists say these links never existed and hence will never be found; evolutionists say they did exist and may or may not be found. Since the supposed or actual appearance of most species must have taken place in the distant past the only place to look for the necessary evidence is in the fossil record. Creationists point out that the links required by evolutionists have not come to light in spite of decades of diligent search by those who sincerely wish to find them. Furthermore the claim is that entirely hypothetical forms are introduced on a wholesale basis to fill the gaps. Evolutionists reply that many good links have already been found and that fossilization, being a very haphazard process, cannot be expected to supply a complete and perfect record of all beings that lived in the past. The key question becomes, just how good or how bad is the fossil record. Some students regard it as surprisingly good, others as woefully bad; everyone wishes it could be better. The paleontologists have found enough to encourage them to keep digging and they seldom come home empty-handed. Whatever else may be said about the fossil record it must always improve.

Anyone who thinks about the problem should contemplate the hazards that determine the fate of any products of the past. Consider the works and bodies of men. It is known that Rome was a city of millions of inhabitants—how many skeletons of those millions that lived only two thousand years ago are now to be

Fig. 24-3 Fossils abound. (a) Trilobites from the Cambrian Period, specimens about one-half inch long; (b) Petrified tree standing in position of growth, Yellowstone Park, Wyoming; (c) Spiny marine brachiopods from the Devonian Period, etched by acid from limestone, specimens about one inch across; (d) Dinosaur tracks in the roof of a Utah coal mine that have been cleaned of coaly covering, not painted.

(a) W.L. Stokes (b) Erling Dorf (c) U.S. Geological Survey (d) James Balsley.

found? And how many Athenians, or Alexandrians, or Babylonians? What is preserved of most ancient civilizations are things more durable than flesh and bone. Were it not for monuments of stone and artifacts of baked clay, metal and glass we would know but little of many great cultures of the past. Of the primitive nomadic tribes that once roamed North America the only really plentiful traces are arrow and spear points of stone. One might suppose that these durable objects were all that these ancient people made or possessed. And where would one go to find specimens of the bison that roamed the plains by millions along with the makers of the lances and arrows?

There are exceptions to the general scarcity of relics of human history and these are of great importance. Artifacts of the Egyptian civilization which flourished in a dry climate are relatively abundant. Here are objects of wood, papyrus, and fiber along with those of stone. Then too the practice of embalming has preserved hundreds of human bodies that would have otherwise gone the way of all flesh.

Critics of the pre-human or prehistoric record should honestly try to be realistic about the state of the fossil record. What can be expected to remain of living things after the passage of thousands, millions, hundreds of millions, even billions of years? Consider that to become a fossil, a dinosaur, for example, must have been buried immediately after death, petrified or otherwise preserved from decay as it lay within the earth, protected from the destructive effects of extreme heat and pressure, exposed at the proper time by erosion without being disintegrated by soil-forming processes, and finally at the last minute rescued by an intelligent human being with the interest and knowledge to reconstruct and study it. Small wonder that those who have considered the matter would conclude that for every fossil known, literally thousands or tens of thousands once existed and have disappeared without a trace.

As with human remains and artifacts there are exceptions to the general scarcity of plant and animal fossils. When conditions are right a fairly complete sample of the life of particular areas is buried and preserved. The famous Tar Pits of Los Angeles is a good example. Here in addition to the large and

Fig. 24-4 Fossil bones at the La Brea tar pits, Los Angeles, California. Most of these packed remains pertain to mammals trapped in natural springs of tar that ooze from sources in the rocks beneath. About half of the species represented are extinct; the age is estimated at about 15,000 years. Los Angeles County Museum of Natural History.

spectacular mammals there are many smaller ones, together with birds, reptiles, and amphibians. There are numerous insects and a variety of plants including large trees. All the forms that are found together constitute a unified, natural assemblage compatible with a specific climate and topographic setting. Fairly complete and balanced groups of fossil organisms have come to light at practically all levels of the past. It is to these that the student of evolution turns for much of his evidence. Like King Tutankhamen's tomb they throw light on certain times that far surpasses the general run of evidence.

Another truth should be borne in mind. Someone said it well: *The beginnings of all things are small.* In every lineage of living things no matter how fragmentary it may be the earliest members are small; thus, small shellfish, small reptiles, including small dinosaurs, small horses and small monkeys. As one would expect, a small thing is less likely to be preserved than a large one. Not only were the first members of the individual lineages small in size but they were small in numbers. No matter what one may believe about the origins of any group it is contrary to all evidence, even scriptural, to suppose that it started with a large number of identical things. At first there were a few; then if these proved successful, natural increase would bring larger numbers. Human experience verifies this; at first there were only a few Romans, or a few Americans—later there were millions.

These are the reasons why many critical links have not been and may never be found. It is in the transition from one group to another that the fossil record is weak and on this point the creationists have concentrated their attack. This is excellent tactics. No matter how many links are found there will be many still missing. Only when each creature of the past can come forth with a birth certificate attached will a die-hard critic be fully convinced.

GENETICS—EACH AFTER HIS KIND

A complete history of biology might be written in terms of the gradual discovery of how reproduction of living things is accomplished. Much of a practical nature was known in prehistoric time; both plants and animals were domesticated and the production of certain desirable types was insured by selective breeding of animals and the collection, preservation and planting of superior seeds. Eggs, sperm and seeds were known to act in some mysterious way to carry the essence of inheritance but even Charles Darwin was far from the truth in his understanding of how it all operates.

Cells were discovered in 1665 by Robert Hooke but the theory that all living things consist of cells was not published until 1838. Shortly thereafter, in 1845, von Siebold declared that protozoa are simply animals that consist of single cells. Rudolf Virchow asserted that all cells must come from previous cells. Cell division and multiplication constitute an observable manifestation of reproduction; and with the discovery of the minute threadlike chromosomes in the nucleus of cells during the 1870s the relation of cell division to the reproduction of the complete organism began to unfold. Next came the discovery in the period 1910-1920 that chromosomes consist of still smaller entities which were called genes and that these are the bearers of unit hereditary traits.

Attention then shifted from purely descriptive and observational matters to the physical and chemical bases of inheritance. Careful research established the fact that a remarkable substance in the nucleus of the cell called deoxyribonucleic acid or DNA is the ultimate hereditary determiner. The discovery of the composition and structure of DNA in 1953 may be the crowning contribution of biology. With the discovery of the famed double helix and the manner in which it replicates itself came the realization of what must precede the division of all cells and what ultimately carries the essence of inheritance from one generation to the next. No matter which of many means of reproduction an organism may depend on, the replication of DNA within it is basic. This is what assures that all things multiply after their kind.

Mankind consists of males and females and the well-known sexual processes of human reproduction may obscure the fact that there are many other very effective ways in which lesser beings perpetuate themselves. Everyone with an elemental knowledge of hygiene is familiar with diseases brought on by viruses, bacteria and protozoans. Viruses are the most simple. They consist of little more than the DNA and accompanying RNA needed to reproduce but they must get inside the cells they infect in order to multiply. Bacterial diseases are caused by the multiplication of entire cells; the same is true of the protozoan infections. The reproduction of single-celled organisms that cause disease differs in no essential way from that of their numerous harmless relatives. The basis for their multiplication is the

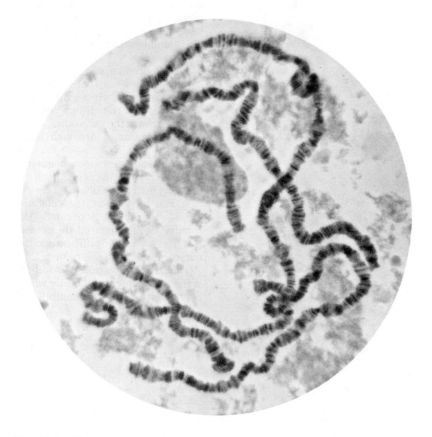

Fig. 24-5   Chromosomes of the fruit fly. These have been stained with organic dye and highly magnified to show the individual segments or genes.

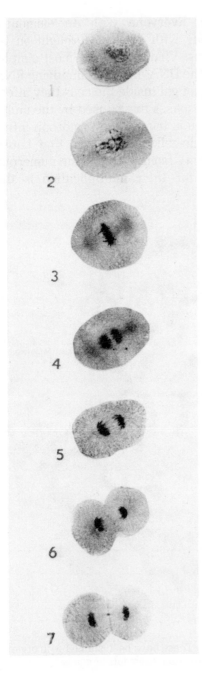

Fig. 24-6 Cell division—each after his kind.

1. A normal cell. At this stage the genetic material, seen as a dark aggregation in the center of the cell, is surrounded by a thin nuclear membrane.

2. Beginning of cell division. The genetic material is beginning to form into dense, stringlike chromosomes while asters (radiating strands at the poles of the nucleus) are becoming visible.

3. The stage is set for cell division. The chromosomes have thickened, and the strands radiating from the asters have joined to form the spindle which enmeshes the chromosomes.

4. Cell division under way. The chromosomes have split lengthwise and one of each pair migrates or is drawn along the fibers of the spindle toward the cell walls.

5. Chromosomes are well separated.

6. Chromosomes are completely separated and the cell itself is pinching in at the midline.

7. End of division; the cells are almost completely separated, the spindle has disappeared, the genetic material is becoming diffuse and the nuclear membrane will reform.

This process, variously modified, is the only known method by which reproduction is accomplished among living things.

division of the genetic material followed by the splitting of the cell. Cells may split lengthwise or crosswise or by breaking into a number of equal parts. Yeast cells, employed by man to create carbon dioxide in making bread, divide rapidly into numerous bud-like reproductions of the original. All these methods are said to be asexual as there is no difference between the products of reproduction.

The asexual method of reproduction also carries through hundreds of types of many-celled organisms. Budding is common; new individuals begin as branches or buds from the parent. The repulsive tapeworm may break into segments and each segment can become a new individual. From creeping lateral growths (stolons) new strawberry plants spring up to become separate from the parent when the stolon disintegrates.

Spores too are asexual. They are exceedingly small and dust-like and may be dispersed in water or air. Each is capable of becoming a new individual. Thousands of plants reproduce in this manner. It is their very smallness that enables them to spread widely; but no matter how small they are the genetic material inside is complete. One more method of asexual reproduction that deserves mention is parthenogenesis. Here an unfertilized egg of a normally sexual type of organism is somehow stimulated to give rise to a complete individual.

Sexual reproduction has many advantages and is the method of the higher plants and animals. Here two individuals, generally termed male and female, must join or in some way exchange genetic material. Sperms and eggs are usually but not necessarily involved. Lowly plants and animals show the beginnings of sex when they exchange genetic material in the process of partal fusion or conjugation. Complete fusion is called syngamy.

The most successful forms of sexual reproduction involve the specialization of two sexual elements (gametes), one small and motile, the other larger and well supplied with nutrient. The former are called sperms, the latter eggs. In plants the eggs usually remain attached to the parent while the sperm must be transported in one way or another to reach the egg. Thus the pollen of plants may be carried by water, by air currents and by insects or larger animals. Examples are known to every observant person.

Animals must, in effect, solve the same problem as the plants in bringing together the male and female gametes. Those with external fertilization have instincts and methods for releasing the sexual products near each other, generally in water but this method is extremely wasteful. A female codfish is known to produce 6,000,000 eggs in a single season; only a few are fertilized; and of these in turn only a very small fraction become adult fish. Internal fertilization is clearly less wasteful. Here the eggs and sperms are placed in close proximity so that fertilization is generally assured without waste. Small wonder that two very successful groups of animals, insects and mammals, employ this method.

The many complicated processes and behavior patterns that bring about the mixing of genetic material cannot be discussed further. They are described in any good biology text. Many other topics must also be passed over lightly. One of these, called polyploidy is extremely important in producing new varieties of plants. It is a condition in which three or more complete sets of chromosomes are present in each cell. This multiplication of genetic material arises spontaneously and gives rise to plant types that are mutually fertile with each other but not with the parent from which they arose. Perhaps over one-third of the flowering plants have had this origin. The intricate subject of hybridization is one of great significance in horticulture and animal husbandry. Hybrids may be looked at as proving that the genetic material is both stable and plastic. It was with hybrids that Mendel proved the inheritance of unit characters. Where would the human race be without proper attention to the hybrids that have appeared naturally or been induced artificially in plants and animals? Grafting, which seems to have been practiced since ancient times, is yet another process that shows the importance of the genetic material. The desired characters are carried in the twigs or buds that are grafted onto stock with less desirable traits. In the terminal cells of the grafts is the material that will grow and produce what is wanted.

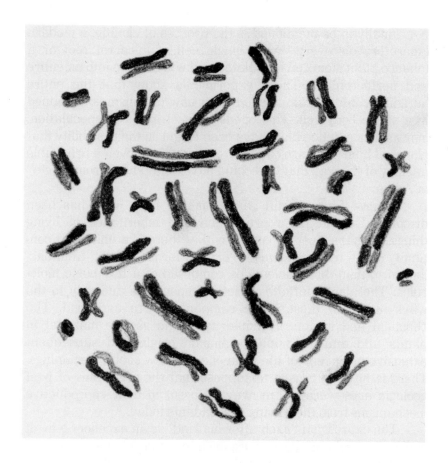

Fig. 24-7 Human chromosomes. As shown in this semidiagrammatic representation, human chromosomes appear in pairs like short pieces of twisted spaghetti. They take on this appearance in the process of cell division; during the resting phase the same genetic material is dispersed and unorganized. In the paired stage the chromosomes are treated chemically to arrest cell division and to enlarge and disentangle the individual pairs so they can be separated and counted.

Human cells have 23 pairs of chromosomes — 46 in all. Each chromosome contains numerous genes; the entire aggregation contains "instructions" for the development of a complete human being. Ideally each of the trillions of cells in the body contains a complete set of genes but only the sex cells carry on the process of reproduction. Every species has its unique genetic material but in the simpler forms of life it is not as highly organized into genes and chromosomes. It is through the genetic material and in no other way that all things reproduce "after their kind."

Finally to be mentioned is the process of cloning, a modern laboratory discovery. Every single cell of a carrot root or a tobacco plant stem can be isolated and will develop into an entire and perfect plant. These experiments show that the entire hereditary information needed for a new organism is contained in a single body cell. This opens up vast areas of speculation; many science fiction plots have been based on the possibility that clones of human beings can be created. Here is even a believable analogy of the way that God could have created Eve from a "rib" of Adam.

Several fundamental truths emerge from what has been discovered about the reproduction and inheritance of living things. Perhaps most important is that there is a unity and continuity of life from its lowest to highest forms. All life, from bacterium to man, has nucleotides composed of a few basic molecules. The almost infinite variety of species is due only to the ways in which these basic components are arranged. The chemical and structural similarity of the genetic material in plants and animals implies common origin and subsequent extensive branching of life from one or a few simple beginnings. There is no good reason to suppose that the organisms of past geologic ages were in any way different in their reproductive mechanisms from their living descendants today.

The expression "each after his kind" is an excellent way of saying that each and every organism must develop according to the store of genetic material it receives from its parent or parents. One may or may not read into this the possibility of variations along the way, but nature and scripture agree in this —there is no other way except by inheritance from one's own kind that anything can reproduce. No matter what else may be said, the very fact that nature displays her most intricate designs and subtle processes in connection with reproduction proves the importance of passing on undamaged genetic material from parent to offspring at all costs. I for one prefer to believe that this is the profound truth intended by the statement "each after his kind." Those who believe that this phrase serves only to warn us that species must never evolve should consider whether or not they are getting the entire message.

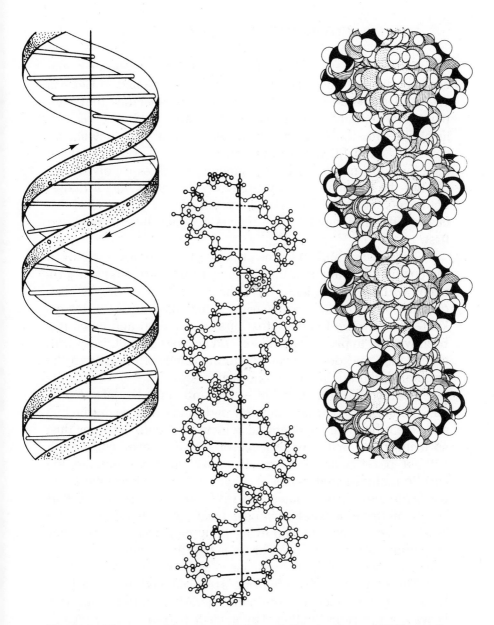

Fig. 24-8 Three graphic representations of the structure of DNA usually referred to as the double helix. (From Stanley L. Miller and Leslie E. Orgel, *The Origins of Life on the Earth* [Englewood Cliffs, N.J.: Prentice-Hall, Inc., 1974], p. 71.)

COMMENTS AND REFERENCES

Two statements of Genesis pertain to the populating of the earth by living things. The first of these, mentioned in Genesis 1:11 and repeated several times thereafter specifies that both plants and animals reproduce "after their kind." The second, mentioned for the first time in Genesis 1:22 is that they should "multiply" and fill the waters and earth. It is true that these directives are not repeated in connection with every division of life but the implication is that they are intended for all things. Both are very basic and closely related but for purposes of discussion the statement "after their kind" has been considered first.

Those who think in terms of literal translations have taken the position that any and all things were made by God to reproduce without deviations throughout time with no mixing, crossing, or evolution whatsoever. In fact the phrase "after his kind" has become the chief text of anti-evolution and much has been written to prove that "kinds" do not and cannot cross with other kinds and do not give rise to anything different from the original kind brought forth in the beginning.

Granted that the term "after his kind" may be defended as anti-evolutionary one cannot help wondering if a more productive and scientific meaning might have been intended. Consider this: no living thing in the experience of man has ever come forth without parents or forebears from which it has derived the genetic material that makes it what it is. Ancient people knew nothing about chromosomes and DNA but we know today that genetic material is what *must* pass from parent to offspring and is what determines that no living thing can come in any other way than "after its kind." This is a fruitful thought because it can be tested by study of organisms at all levels of complexity.

The ways in which offspring are produced are amazingly varied and the subject is a profound one. All modern biology textbooks discuss reproduction. The subject is treated on a college level by C. A. Villee, *Biology*, Saunders; C. G. Simpson, C. S. Pittendrig, and L. H. Tiffany, 1957, *Life: an Introduction to Biology*, Harcourt, Brace; and W. T. Keeton, 1972, *Biological*

Science, 2nd ed., W. W. Norton. No single book dealing with all methods by which "kinds" reproduce appears to have been written.

Those interested in the development of knowledge of genetics and genetic material will find the following books informative: Hans Stubbe, 1973, *History of Genetics,* (translated by E. J. R. Waters), M.I.T. Press; Robert Olby, 1974, *The Path of the Double Helix,* University of Washington Press; and Franklyn H. Portugal and Jack S. Cohen, 1977, *A Century of DNA: A History of the Discovery of the Structure and Function of the Genetic Substance,* M.I.T. Press. A short semi-popular article, "The new genetics: the threads of life," by George W. Beadle appears in the 1964 *Encyclopedia Britannica Book of the Year.* Another excellent 3-part article under the title, "The new biology," is found in *The National Geographic Magazine,* Sept. 1976.

... BE FRUITFUL ... MULTIPLY ...

> And God blessed them, saying, *Be fruitful*, and
> *multiply*, and *fill the waters* in the seas, and let
> fowl multiply in the earth.
>
> Genesis 1:22

Here, as in all matters relating to the creation of living things, the account given in Genesis speaks of God's decrees as though they took effect in the very instant or day in which they were proclaimed. However, reasons have been given for believing that Genesis 1 deals with preparations only, and Genesis 2 tells of the actual appearance of living things.

The expression "be fruitful and multiply" is repeated in connection with mankind: "And God blessed them and said unto them, *Be fruitful and multiply and replenish the earth*, and subdue it. . . ." (Genesis 1:28.) Still later, after the flood, it is recorded that God instructed Noah:

> Bring forth with thee every living thing that is with thee, of all
> flesh, both of fowl, and of cattle, and of every creeping thing that
> creepeth upon the earth; that they may breed abundantly in the
> earth, and *be fruitful, and multiply upon the earth.*
>
> Genesis 8:17

One is almost inclined to ask why God should have found it necessary to command any living thing to multiply and be fruitful. Powerful inner drives would seem to make such a command unnecessary. Ask any student of biology to state in one phrase the most universal law of existence among living things and he must certainly reply: self-preservation. From the simple escape reactions of an amoeba to the reasoned efforts of a human being the urge to remain alive is basic. Although preservation of the individual is often considered to be a matter separate from preservation of the race, the distinction in the end, is almost

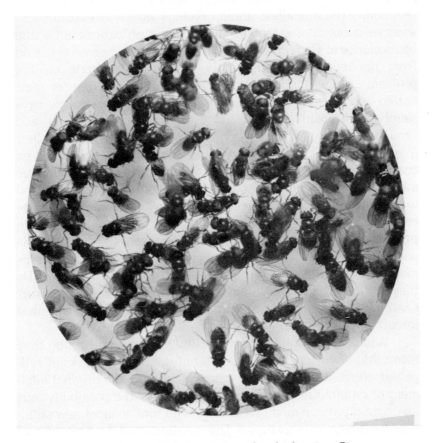

Fig. 25-1   Demonstrating superior powers of multiplication, flies are among the most prolific creatures on earth. Over 500 species combine to add to the miseries of man by biting him, destroying his food, and spreading his diseases. Anything the "breeds like flies" must be doing well in fulfilling the biblical command to "multiply and replenish" the earth.

(Courtesy Turtox. Inc.)

meaningless. One without the other is of no avail. Compared with the urge to reproduce and the urge to maintain the self, all other struggles are minor. The existence of any animal must be short indeed if it put forth no efforts to maintain life and one brief generation is all that could possibly result if there were no inborn urge to reproduce.

The struggle to survive brings into use all the many devices and reactions which living things possess. That these devices and reactions exist in endless and marvelous variety is explained by some as a result of evolution, by others as an expression of the benevolence of God. Probably nothing separates believers in God from non-believers more neatly than their attitude on the problem of how plants and animals came to be suited for their varied modes and places of existence. The Creationist says simply and positively that living things were designed and brought forth by God in possession of everything needful for their existence. The Evolutionist says that organisms are modified by reactions between their environments of life and the genetic material within their bodies. Extreme creationism requires God to give personal attention to every species; extreme evolutionism requires no God at all. How unfortunate that in their zeal to promote one argument or the other the possibility of a reasonable compromise is seldom considered by the antagonists. Perhaps more consideration should be given to the basic scriptures. Do they really prohibit evolution and require strict creationism? Certainly they were given with serious intent. What was that intent?

When the scriptures say "multiply and replenish" do they mean that each species is to carry out the difficult tasks of self-preservation and racial propagation with only the original allotment of capabilities? Or do scriptures allow the possibility that an original pattern might be altered with time to meet new situations as they inevitably arise? The wording itself does not specify one or the other. Perhaps the Parable of the Talents may have meaning here. He who made no efforts to improve or build upon his original gifts lost everything. So it seems to have been in nature. Species that have not adapted are dead. Yes, "dead as a dinosaur," has become a reference to those things which are

ON

THE ORIGIN OF SPECIES

BY MEANS OF NATURAL SELECTION,

OR THE

PRESERVATION OF FAVOURED RACES IN THE STRUGGLE FOR LIFE.

BY CHARLES DARWIN, M.A.,

FELLOW OF THE ROYAL, GEOLOGICAL, LINNÆAN, ETC., SOCIETIES;
AUTHOR OF 'JOURNAL OF RESEARCHES DURING H. M. S. BEAGLE'S VOYAGE
ROUND THE WORLD.'

LONDON:

JOHN MURRAY. ALBEMARLE STREET.

1859.
P. ऽ.

The right of Translation is reserved.

Fig. 25-2   Title page of the first edition of *On the Origin of Species by Means of Natural Selection or the Preservation of Favored Races in the Struggle for Life,* published by Charles Darwin in 1859. This work has been reprinted many times and is said to be the most influential nontheological book ever written. It may in time be regarded as essentially faith promoting.

outmoded and extinct. And consider what is known about the genes, those marvelous devices that shape the individual and carry traits of all kinds from one generation to the next. They seem to be constructed along very rigid lines and yet can be altered in both beneficial and harmful ways. This possibility of altering the genetic material is a fact of nature, but strict creationists do not admit that alterations, no matter how long continued or added upon, are able to produce new "kinds" from old kinds. This topic has been discussed at greater length at an appropriate place in the chapter "After His Kind."

One reason many religious persons have difficulty in accepting Darwin's theory of evolution is that constant deadly struggle is at the heart of it. Scientists may describe the fight for life in terms such as "natural selection" and "survival of the fittest," but the fact remains that death in all its varied forms is an essential ingredient. This is upsetting to those who believe in a loving beneficent Creator. Nevertheless, everyone, no matter what his religious beliefs may be, should be reminded that the struggle for existence is a fact of nature and Charles Darwin merely put it into a reasonable perspective.

Darwin arrived at a logical explanation for fossils and for the widespread waste of life when he considered two obvious facts of nature. The first of these is an overproduction of individuals in all species. This means that many more seeds, spores, eggs, embryos and young individuals are produced than can ever reach adulthood. One species of fern can yield 30 million spores in one season and an ordinary corn plant sends forth 18 million pollen grains during its reproductive cycle. A single fish can spawn as many as 120 million eggs and a female frog lays about 20,000 eggs every year. It has been calculated that if all the offspring of a single pair of flies remained alive and reproduced at an ordinary rate they would produce a mass of flies as large as the earth in a matter of only a few years.

Since only a relatively few of the plants and animals started in life ever reach a stage where they in turn can reproduce the obvious fate of most individuals is death. Many die without a struggle; seeds do not struggle, they fall, as well described in the Parable of the Sower, on all types of soil where only a few sur-

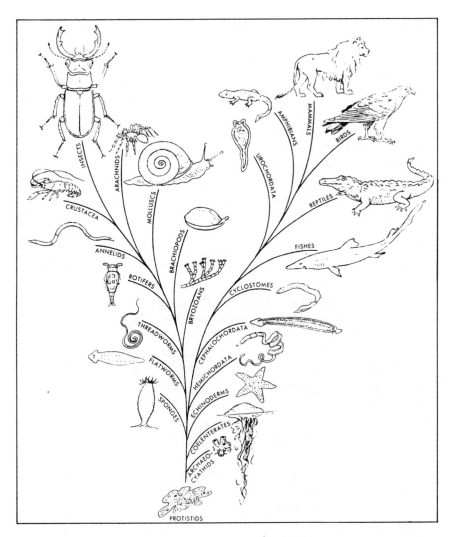

Fig. 25-3   Generalized "tree of life" as visualized by biologists. Progressively more complex animals are portrayed from the lowest stem to the highest branches. Creationists object to such a diagram with connecting lines or branches because it implies evolution of one "kind" to another. Biologists and geologists insist that the evidence of fossils shows an undeniable progression from simple in older rocks to complex in younger ones. To them this is evidence of organic evolution. Creationists deny that it is proof that the life of one age descended from that of a previous one. [From William Lee Stokes, Sheldon Judson, and M. Dane Picard, *Introduction to Geology* (Englewood Cliffs, N.J.: Prentice-Hall, Inc., 1958), p. 359.]

vive. Likewise eggs are totally defenseless and are sought out and devoured by countless hungry enemies. The struggle never lets up; at every stage of existence an animal or plant is subject to passive or active aggression by others of its own and other species and to perils brought on by the non-living forces of nature.

No measure of soft-hearted sentimentality can lessen the fact of a vast waste of life that goes on everywhere among all living things. Furthermore death is brought about by every conceivable means: starvation, disease, predation, and out-and-out bloody combat between and within species. The means may seem repulsive and unworthy of God but it is evidently the results that count. Let those who think in theological terms explain the sufferings of men, the salvation of the good and the damnation of the bad as they criticize the concept of the survival of the fittest in the natural world.

These are grim thoughts; but the directive to "multiply and replenish" would seem to lead inevitably to struggle and competition. As Malthus pointed out, the resources of the earth are limited while the power to reproduce is not. Consequently nothing can multiply unopposed. Some must give way, many must die. To borrow a phrase: Many are called but few are chosen. The thought is a good one for evolutionists as well as creationists.

COMMENTS AND REFERENCES

The subject of biological reproduction has been discussed in chapter 24 in connection with the "after his kind" biblical texts. How reproduction takes place is no longer a mystery; and why offspring resemble their parents is now explained in a natural way. These factual matters can be thought of as a field entirely separate from organic evolution. That individuals are born, grow and die is known to even the most ignorant and unlearned; that species appear, develop and disappear is much less apparent but no less real. The difference is one of time and human perspective. Individual lives are short; racial lives are so long that they are not comprehensible without taking into account the evidence of fossils and the long-term implications of genetics. Again the subject is vast and to the non-specialist, utterly bewildering. This chapter is an attempt to justify the thought that the command, admonition and blessing to multiply and replenish the earth applies to more than day-to-day reproduction. It clearly seems to do more than merely approve the idea of organic evolution. In the end the creation of new species appears to be the way that life has multiplied and filled the earth.

The topic of evolution was introduced in chapter 18 in connection with the origin of life; references given there were not intended to enlarge on the subject of what happened after life got under way. Looking ahead, the origin and evolution of man will be treated very briefly in chapter 31. Again the references do not cover the subject of organic evolution as a general process.

For those willing to give the controversial subject of organic evolution a fair hearing the best place to commence is the classical book by Charles Darwin, "*On The Origin of Species by Means of Natural Selection or the Preservation of Favored Races in the Struggle for Life,*" published in 1859. There have been numerous editions and the book is widely available. From this basic beginning the field widens and the choices are difficult. A widely recommended but slightly outdated book is G. G. Simpson, 1953, *The Major Features of Evolution*, Columbia University Press. Probably nothing ever produced in popular printed form exceeds in total impact the series entitled *The World We Live In* issued by *Life* magazine in the interval Dec. 8, 1952 to Dec. 20, 1954. The 13 parts of the series were reissued in a book of the same title by Time, Incorporated in 1955. In the articles and book the succession of life is discussed and illustrated with special emphasis on the Age of Reptiles and Age of Mammals; the illustrations are as authentic as it is possible to achieve. A second book, *The Wonders of Life on Earth*, was issued by Time, Incorporated in 1960. It too is lavishly illustrated and in reality is an updated commentary on the research and contributions of Charles Darwin.

Another widely available reference is the Life Nature Library, a series of 18 volumes by recognized authorities issued by Time Incorporated. The diversity of life is emphasized. The volume titled *Evolution* issued in 1964 is particularly informative.

Another set of books from the same source is the Emergence of Man Library; the volume *Life Before Man*, 1972, gives the evolutionary background of man. Other than this, the remaining volumes treat the progress of man as man. Probably the best survey of the fossil evidence is "Evolution and the Fossil Record," a selection of papers from the *Scientific American* with an introduction by Leo F. Laporte, Freeman, 1978. The entire September 1978 issue of *Scientific American* is devoted to the subject of organic evolution. This is essentially the latest (not last) word on the subject.

Those who find the concept of organic evolution unacceptable should study the writings of creationists. Many books, pamphlets, tapes and courses of study are available from Creation-Life Publishers, P. O. Box 15666, San Diego, California 92115.

...BEHOLD IT WAS VERY GOOD

And God saw every thing that he had made,
and, behold, it was very good.

Genesis 1:31

I t would be surprising if God should declare his creations anything but good. What is surprising is that man frequently judges these same creations to be bad. The theological explanation usually given is that the creations of God were perfectly good to begin with and that the badness that now exists is due to the Fall of Adam and other sins of mankind. In the minds of many this places on Adam the blame for everything that isn't to their liking. The "thorns and thistles" that sprang up to torment and afflict man were accompanied by endless other evils such as mosquitoes, rattlesnakes, and bubonic plague. The contrast between the original goodness of creation and the present imperfect state of the world reaches its extreme expression in the so-called "no death before the Fall" doctrine which is held by some theologians. According to this idea the world before the Fall was not only perfect in every sense it was also free of death. Nothing was dying, each individual plant and animal continued in its original perfection without reproduction until the curse of Adam fell upon it. Yes, Adam's transgression brought death into the world not only for himself and his descendants but also for all other living things. Most churches do not go this far; but by interpreting the scriptures in literal ways they manage to throw on

Adam and Eve most of the blame for everything that they consider to be wrong with the earth and mankind.

Books have been written on how sin originated, how it changed the world and how original perfection has deteriorated to present imperfection. Only a few additional comments in connection with the topic of creation can be given here. In the first place, it was God who pronounced his creations good and we must certainly grant that he knows better than we do what is good and what is not. That which is satisfactory or excellent in our selfish human, earth-centered view may not be good in the eternal, heaven-centered view of God, the Creator. Like children, it is doubtful we know what is really good for ourselves let alone for any greater purposes.

Fig. 26-1   The Garden of Eden as portrayed in a once popular book, *The Work Days of God,* by Herbert W. Morris, published in 1877. Few biblical subjects have been rendered more often than Adam and Eve in the paradisiacal surroundings where they began their lives on earth. Inasmuch as the Garden of Eden is visualized as the ultimate expression of God's preparation for man it is easy to believe that this was the condition of the earth when he declared it to be very good.

This thought is clearly unscriptural. God declared his work not only to be very good but also completed before the watering of the earth. He "planted" the garden in which things grew naturally after the watering.

Only a childish mind would want to live in a world without challenge, opposition and trial. Shakespeare wrote: "For as you know, security is mortal's chiefest enemy." The essence of Darwinian evolution is survival of the fittest; living things with or without man are to the biologist largely the outcome of ages of trial, endless struggle and ruthless elimination of the unfit. The impersonal, unthinking forces of nature bring trials to every living thing. Man to a large extent can avoid the trials of lesser beings but he can conscientiously choose to undergo trials of a higher nature. He can embark willingly upon programs of self-improvement including the greatest of all, enlistment in the plan to bring forth the Kingdom of God.

What was the status of things when they were pronounced good? The clue is that the declaration was made at the end of the

Fig. 26-2   A photograph of the barren surface of Mars taken from a space vehicle in 1978. This view probably represents what the earth looked like when God, at the end of the sixth day, pronounced it to be good. The planet Mars is now essentially waterless but many scientists believe it could produce water if it should pass through a molten stage. Earth was also once dry and acquired its supply of surface water as a consequence of having melted.
(Courtesy NASA.)

sixth day, not in the seventh day. Consider that man was not here —his physical creation is distinctly an event of the seventh day. Considering also that it had not yet rained upon the earth, it is inconceivable that land vegetation could have been in existence. The earth was apparently lifeless, barren and uninhabited by any higher forms of life. Yet God pronounced it good! Earth was certainly far from being a paradise in the human sense at this stage of existence but it had the potential of becoming one. Clearly, that which man considers good and beautiful is less basic and important than that which will later become good and beautiful.

The wisdom, might, power, and intelligence of God are shown more abundantly in the establishment of a system that was bound to succeed than it could possibly be by any series of mighty works that had to be imposed upon an imperfect system already in existence. As long as man equates his works such as the building of dams, the digging of canals and the planting of fields with the creative works of God he will never appreciate what God has done or how it was accomplished. I know of no more perceptive statement than that of Charles Kingsley:

> We know of old that God was so great that he could make all things, but behold He is so much greater even than that, that He can make all things make themselves.

COMMENTS AND REFERENCES

The goodness of God's creations have inspired expressions of human praise and admiration throughout recorded history. Surely the greatest compliment to be paid a creator is to study his creations. It is the point of this chapter that God was satisfied and pleased with his efforts long before they bore fruit in the world as man knows it. That this is so is an undeniable indication of the relationship between Genesis 1 and Genesis 2 and the wisdom of what appears to be two accounts of creation.

An interesting chapter in the history of science and theology is the *Bridgewater Treatises*. A wish of Francis H. Egerton, eighth Earl of Bridgewater, who died in 1829, as expressed in his will, was to find and support eight scientific authors capable of demonstrating "the Power, Wisdom, and Goodness of God, as manifested in the Creation." Eight great volumes, carrying out this wish were published in England between 1838 and 1870. As human statements for the goodness of God's ultimate creations, the *Bridgewater Treatises* are unsurpassed. However, their arguments have largely crumbled. Natural processes have proven perfectly capable of producing the effects which men have piously ascribed to God. It is by calling on divine or super-natural influences to explain that which may later be shown to be natural that well-meaning men have greatly weakened the concept of God as a creator. Modern creationists and funda-mentalists would do well to study the arguments of their prede-cessors — and not repeat the fallacious ones.

The idea that all things can and do develop in inevitable or predestined ways is an old one in religion, philosophy, and science. A central aspect of Plato's philosophy is the division of the universe in two parts. Although he did not make the connec-tion clear he saw a world of change and becoming on one hand and a world of eternal, immutable things on the other. The immutable things he called "Ideas" or "Forms." Aristotle, student of Plato and the greatest biologist of ancient time, also recognized a distinction between the potential and the actual. In the seed and embryo he saw the possibility of the fully developed organism. In all things he distinguished "matter from form, the relatively raw stuff from the finished product." These philoso-phers were not, however, greatly concerned with the ultimate beginning of lineages or generations — they accepted man as man and not as a development from something less.

Science today portrays the universe, the earth, life in general and man in particular as having resulted from a long line of natural cause-and-effect events. This has been a great irony of history — the need for God as a supernatural creator has gradually faded away. Disillusionment and disappointment exist in spite of finding every aspect of creation amazing and awe inspiring, even faith promoting. The disappointment comes in finding no one along the line or behind the scenes producing the miracles that we had been told about and were expecting. To many the creator has become a "hydrogen god" or a "big-bang god"—far too remote and impersonal to have concern for man.

Genesis, when properly understood, has the antidote for despair. The glory of God's creative power is that he knows and commands his materials so well that once they are organized the desired results must follow no matter how complex the process or long-delayed the outcome. Here, plainer than in any philosophy, is the demonstration that there are two levels of being, the potential and the actual.

CHAPTER

27

...EVENING AND MORNING...
SIXTH DAY...

And the evening and the morning were the
sixth day.

Genesis 1:31

W hen the earth was a glowing molten sphere it could not be
said to have had a dark side and a light side. Later, when it
cooled and a crust formed a new arrangement for separating
light from darkness took effect. The sun lighted one side and left
the other in shadow. The lighted side of the earth, or of any other
sun-lighted planet, is generally said to be experiencing day while
the dark side is experiencing night. Many different arrange-
ments of night and day exist among the planets of the solar
system and others can be imagined. Mercury has a "day" equal
to almost 59 earth days; during the period of light, temperatures
rise to 610° K. and at night they fall to nearly absolute zero. By
contrast, giant Jupiter has days and nights of about 5 hours each.
This means little, however, since the outer planets are so distant
that they receive only negligible amounts of sunlight.

It is conceivable that the earth could have evolved with one
face permanently toward the sun to create endless day on one
side and endless night on the other. Fortunately for the life that
inhabits it, the earth rotates and every part experiences
alternate periods of light and darkness of approximately equal

length. These alternations are the days and nights with which man is familiar and by which he reckons time. Among the many complicated motions that affect the earth this was probably the last to take effect; it seems to be a most fortunate way to divide light from darkness on the human scale. To paraphrase a biblical verse: was the day made for man or was man made for the day?

The materials that make up the earth were circling the sun long before it became a planet. Revolution continued as the solid constituents were gathered together and compacted, as the earth was bombarded by giant meteorites, and as it melted and solidi-

Fig. 27-1 The earth in half-shadow as photographed from the moon. The division between light and darkness on a rotating sphere creates the days and nights with which man is familiar.
(NASA.)

fied. Over the eons the earth has settled into a remarkably precise time-table—it completes a journey of about 300,000,000
miles in 365 days, 5 hours, 49 minutes, and 12 seconds! Apparently during billions of journeys all irregularities in the system
have been eradicated. So much for the revolution of the earth—
how about its rotation?

Although we can only speculate as to when in its early history the earth began to rotate there is no reason to believe that
it has not been rotating from the time of its final compaction 4.6
billion years ago. At that time and for a billion or so years thereafter a great deal of loose material, some in large chunks, was
still circling the sun. These were gradually gathered up by the
planets leaving vast impact scars to record the process. It seems
likely that some of the bodies that struck the earth were of sufficient size to affect both its revolution and rotation.

A second event cannot fail to have made an impression on
the motions of the earth. This was the melting or liquifaction
event. The sun as a liquid body illustrates the probabilities. It
does not rotate as a solid mass; as shown by keeping track of
sunspots, the equator completes a rotation in 25 hours while the
middle latitudes take about 27 hours. When the earth solidified
for the last time any significant variations in the rotation of the
outside zones came to an end. Within the earth more complicated
motions continue. The molten core rotates at a slightly different
rate than the solid exterior. It lags behind about 13 miles each
year in relation to the surface. This differential movement has
the interesting effect of creating the strong electrical and
magnetic fields of the earth.

The core of the earth is dense and heavy; it is almost certainly composed of iron and nickel. Its outer shell appears to be
molten. The heavy metallic components making up the core are
thought to have settled inward mainly during the molten stage of
earth history. Some believe the core descended rather suddenly
and in so doing contributed to a vast melting and mixing of the
entire globe. In any event the transferal of heavier material to
the center of the earth must have speeded up the rotation. This is
illustrated when a skater or dancer draws in her arms to achieve
a more rapid spin. At the time of core formation the earth may

have been rotating at its most rapid rate. During the past 2 billion years it seems to have been slowing down. Evidence for this comes from surprising sources.

Because of the tilt of its axis the earth goes through a succession of seasons during which any spot becomes alternately cooler and warmer and generally also cooler and drier. These cyclic changes are reflected in growth of plants and animals — the best known effect being tree rings. Similar lines or rings of growth are found in lower orders of plants and in animal bones and shells. Without going into technical details it is fairly well

Fig. 27-2 Nature's time keepers. Upper view shows a cross section of a tree trunk with annual rings. The oldest wood dated by ring counting is about 8,000 years old. Lower left is a natural exposure of partly solidified galacial clay showing light (summer) and dark (winter) layers; the one-foot ruler gives a scale. Such paired layers are called varves, they have been found in deposits of all geological ages. Lower right is a specimen from the oil shale deposits of Utah. The seasonal layers, deposited in a large fresh-water lake, are very thin. About 175 years are estimated for each inch in this formation.

(Upper photo, National Park Service; lower left, J. Hoover Mackin; lower right, photo by James Howell, III.)

established that intervals of days, months (moon cycles) and years are detectable in the growth patterns of living (and fossil) plants and animals. During the Silurian Period, 410 million years ago there were apparently 410 days in the year; in the Pennsylvanian Period about 300 million years ago there were 380 days per year; and in the late Cretaceous, 80 million years ago the count was 370 days. The slowing of the earth's rotation is attributed to the moon. The action is indirect and results from the drag of the lunar tides across shallow sea beds. This effect, working by infinitesimal steps has apparently doubled the length of the day over a period of one and a half billion years. The forecast is that, in the end, the earth will slow to the point where it will present the same face to the moon just as the moon presents the same face to the earth. At this time the rotation of the earth will be the same as its revolution. In the meantime we must live with the thought that the day is being lengthened by a small fraction of a second each year.

28

THESE ARE . . . THE GENERATIONS OF THE HEAVENS AND THE EARTH . . .

> These are the generations of the heavens and
> of the earth when they were created in the day
> that the Lord God made the earth and the
> heavens.
>
> Genesis 2:4

The fourth verse of the second chapter of Genesis is a concise reminder of what took place during the six days of creation. It comes immediately after the assertion that God rested from (or had completed) his creative works. It is followed by the declaration that rain had not fallen upon the earth and that man was not yet here to till the ground. Another indication that verse 4 is intended as a summary is the fact that it refers to the total six days of creation as being one day. Certainly it is not irreverent to imagine that in the mind of God the entire process of creation is one uninterrupted sequence even though it is made up of the series of alternations of light and darkness that he chose to call days.

What a person reaps from this key verse depends on his or her understanding of the term "generation." This is a word with several meanings and unless a student is prepared to accept a less common but wholly acceptable definition in preference to a more common one he may miss the central, most meaningful message of the creation scriptures.

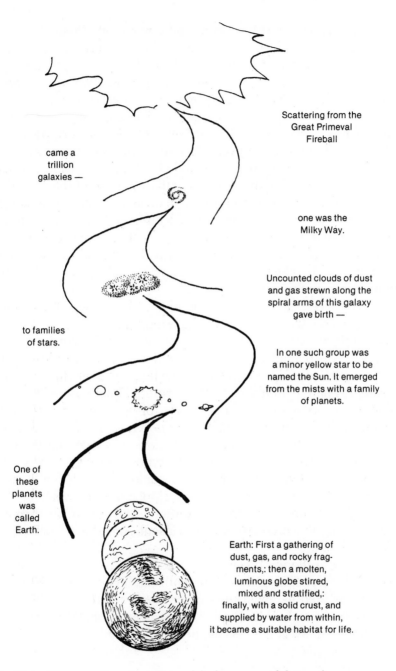

Scattering from the
Great Primeval
Fireball

came a
trillion
galaxies —

one was the
Milky Way.

Uncounted clouds of dust
and gas strewn along the
spiral arms of this galaxy
gave birth —

to families
of stars.

In one such group was
a minor yellow star to be
named the Sun. It emerged
from the mists with a family
of planets.

One of
these
planets
was
called
Earth.

Earth: First a gathering of
dust, gas, and rocky fragments,: then a molten,
luminous globe stirred,
mixed and stratified,:
finally, with a solid crust, and
supplied by water from within,
it became a suitable habitat for life.

Fig. 28-1   These are the generations of the heavens and the earth. . . .

The word generation occurs 64 times in the Bible, the word generations 28 times. In most cases these words refer to the circle of existence from birth to death or to an aggregation of people making up such a circle: "This generation shall not pass away . . ." (Luke 21:32). The remaining usages refer to the successive offspring of specific persons: "These are the generations of Noah . . ." (Genesis 10:1). In the entirety of scripture only Genesis 2:4 unmistakably asserts that inanimate things can have generations in a way analogous to living things. Considering that man was not yet in existence on earth at the end of the sixth day there could have been no begettings or generations of humanity up to that point. The same may be inferred with regard to all other living things — the procreation, begetting or engendering of plants and animals through the natural processes of reproduction was not to take place; in fact, could not take place, until after the watering of the earth.

There should be no doubt about the intended meaning. There is a perfectly valid, legitimate and unmistakable definition that applies. Several dictionary quotations are worth repeating. In the *Oxford English Dictionary* which defines words on historical principles we discover the perfectly obvious thought that a generation is: "that which is generated." Furthermore we find that the process of generation is the bringing into existence of *anything* (substances, animals, etc.). *Webster's Seventh New Collegiate Dictionary* defines generation as: a type or class of objects developed from an earlier type; also (as a verb): the process of coming into being. One could not wish for a more precise and accurate one-word description of the development of the physical universe than "generation." But only if we accept it as meaning the production of a present something from a previous something.

As with the word *generation* the total text of Genesis 2:4 is unmistakably clear and precise. Both the heavens and the earth are designated as generators or producers just as science perceives them to be. And note that whereas only one earth is mentioned there is the possibility of an indefinite number of successive heavens.

Things that are generated by the heavens must be physical entities such as galaxies, suns, and planets. Things generated by the earth must also be in the physical realm including the atmosphere, water and solid entities ranging from continents to rocks and minerals.

The implication seems inescapable; the sequence of events and configurations of matter that produced the earth are evolutionary in the sense that all things unfolded and progressed with the passage of time. This concept was incomprehensible and unacceptable until the present state of scientific knowledge was attained.

...ON THE SEVENTH DAY GOD ENDED
HIS WORK...AND RESTED...

> And on the seventh day God ended his work
> which he had made; and he rested on the seventh
> day from all his work which he had made.
> And God blessed the seventh day, and sancti-
> fied it: because that in it he had rested from all
> his work which God created and made.
>
> Genesis 2:2-3

Christians and Jews learn from their Sunday School lessons that God created the earth in six days and rested on the seventh. The story is told in Genesis and emphasized a number of times in subsequent scripture. Exodus 20:11 states: "For in six days the Lord made heaven and earth, the sea, and all that in them is, and rested on the seventh day. . . ." Hebrews 4:4 says: "For he spake in a certain place of the seventh day on this wise, and God did rest on the seventh day from all his works."

But the matter is not as simple as it is generally presented. There is a critical difference between something being completed *by* a certain day and its being completed *on* that certain day. If anything is clear from the scripture it is that God ended his creative works *on* the seventh day, not *on* the sixth day or even *at the end* of the sixth day. The belief that God's work was finished by the close of the sixth day is clearly contrary to scripture. God both worked and rested on the seventh day. Just when

Fig. 29-1   Genesis 2:4 implies that all of creation was accomplished in one day. Artistic representations such as this from Martin Luther's Bible published in 1534 attempt to show all of creation in one scene.

he ceased the work of creation is not clear but his own word is that he is now resting from creating so that type of work at least is finished.

Despite its unfinished condition the earth was nevertheless almost ready to fill its appointed mission and God had pronounced it good at the end of the sixth day. All the preparations of earth and water were now to take effect. The scene was set for a significant and crucial event—the watering of the earth.

This is probably the best place to examine more closely the question of God's activities on the seventh day as contrasted with those of the previous days. The whole area has been one of misunderstanding and confusion chiefly because the nature of creation itself has been largely incomprehensible. A distinction is evidently to be made between the work of creation and other works of God. God is said to be resting on the seventh day. Note the exact words, God is resting "from all his work which God created and made."

The topic of what constitutes God's work and also his rest has entered into arguments about the age of the earth and the duration of the seventh day. Some maintain that the seventh day isn't over. They argue that even after he had created Adam God did other works such as plant the Garden of Eden and write the Ten Commandments for Moses.

If God is doing work of any kind, the argument continues, then he isn't resting and the seventh day cannot be over. Furthermore, the seventh day must be at least as long as it has been since it started approximately with the appearance of man 6,000 years ago. On the assumption that the 6,000 year period is nearing a close the end of the seventh day of creation is also at hand. In other words, when the seventh day is terminated it will have been 6,000 years long. And if the seventh or last day is 6,000 years long then each of the previous days were probably also that long, giving a total duration of the earth of 36,000 years.

On the other hand there are powerful scriptorians who profess that the seventh day is over. Their argument is based on scriptures such as Genesis 2:2, "He (God) rested on the seventh day from all his work"; Exodus 20:11, "The Lord rested on the seventh day"; Genesis 2:3, "In it (the seventh day) he had rested." Finally, Hebrews 4:4, "God did rest the seventh day from all his works." The reasoning is that since these statements say that God rested on the seventh day but none say that he is *now resting*, his rest period must be over. But note the *full* text of Genesis 2:2-3:

> And on the seventh day God ended his work *which he had made*; and he rested on the seventh day from all his work *which he had made*.

Fig. 29-2 Seven-headed beast described in the Book of Revelation and depicted here by a medieval drawing. Many mystical representations of the number seven, associated with the seventh day, are emphasized in the final book of the Bible.
(Drawing by Albrecht Durer, sixteenth-century artist.)

> And God blessed the seventh day and sanctified it, because
> that in it he had rested from all his work *which God created and
> made.*

The scriptures do give a satisfactory answer to the problem
of the seventh day. Several references including those just cited
tell exactly what it is that God had completed and the work from
which he rested. That which was finished was that which had
been "created and made" or simply that which God had made.
Put in another way, after he pronounced things good he
organized (or made) no more material in the creative sense.
"Thus the heaven and earth *were finished,* and all the host of
them." (Genesis 2:1.) Note that this statement was made *before*
the watering of the earth, and *before* the coming of man.

Surely, God, being what he is, can and does do more than
create. This is only one of his works. How could his tasks be over
when men by the billions were yet to come to earth? An idle God
is inconceivable and so is one who has withdrawn from the scene
or lost interest in man.

Before scriptorians terminate the seventh day or put God in
retirement they should consider where their arguments leave
them. What is to be made of the fact that no mention is made of
an eighth day either in ancient or modern revelations? This
makes one very suspicious that no eighth day exists or is intended in the overall economy of God. By all interpretations the
work of God in relation to man and this temporal earth is to be
finished on the seventh day. The Book of Revelation which God
gave to John "to shew unto his servants things which must
shortly come to pass" describes in allegorical terms the events of
the last days. It is replete with references to the number seven:
seven churches, seven stars, seven last plagues, seven mountains, seven heads, seven eyes, seven horns, seven angels, etc.

One of the significant events of the last days is described
thus:

> And when the seven thunders had uttered their voices, I was
> about to write: and I heard a voice from heaven saying unto me,
> Seal up those things which the seven thunders uttered, and write
> them not.

And the angel which I saw stand upon the sea and upon the earth lifted up his hand to heaven,

And sware by him that liveth for ever and ever, who created heaven, and the things that therein are, and the earth, and the things that therein are, and the sea, and the things which are therein, that there should be time no longer:

Revelation 10:4-6

Is the fact that time will come to an end the reason that there is no eighth day? Eternity is not divided into days. Time exists only when it is measured or measurable. This is the great distinction between time and eternity—time is measured, eternity is not.

There is more; if we are still in the seventh day how long has it already endured? The exact beginning of the seventh day is not specified, but it was marked approximately by the watering of the earth. This is an event that geologists are able to date with considerable assurance. Water produces sedimentary rocks, that is rocks deposited in layers and consisting of worn fragments that collectively are called sand, silt, and gravel. Non-sedimentary rocks such as granite and basalt are produced by igneous action. No sedimentary rocks were found on the moon; igneous rocks are everywhere.

The oldest known rocks of the earth are of igneous types and are dated at almost 4 billion years. The first sedimentary rocks come somewhat later at about 3,500,000,000 years. The evidence is that somewhere between these two dates water appeared on the earth in sufficient quantity to fill oceans and create running streams.

I accept the approximate time of the arrival of water as given by geologists as three and one half billion years ago. On this assumption I base my argument that the seventh day is at least this long. In no other way can I reconcile God's statement that in the seventh day he not only concluded his creative work but also rested or ceased to create. This removes a great cause of contention between those who believe in creationism and those who believe in evolutionism. Creationists rightfully insist that God is the creator but they should realize that so far as this earth is concerned he is not now creating and has not been creating in this particular system for a very long time by human standards. Evolutionists maintain, just as rightly, that they see no evidence of an ongoing creation in the natural world which they have been observing and studying in a scientific way. They must look farther back into the earlier six days of creation for evidences of the creative activity of God.

Faced with the fantastic, awe-inspiring phenomenon of the universe men have had to choose between belief that it runs itself with no need for a creator and belief that it cannot run itself or exist without a creator. Both views are possible because neither takes in the total view of things. They conflict for the same reason. There can be no reconciliation if evolutionists are not allowed time and space in which to fit their facts of observation, experience, and experimentation. Creationists must likewise be

Fig. 29-3   Representation of the pouring out of the seven vials of the wrath of God as described in chapter 16 of the Book of Revelation. From an illustrated Luther Bible published in 1523.

The major divisions, with brief explanations of each, are shown in the following scale of relative geologic time, which is arranged in chronological order with the oldest division at the bottom, the youngest at the top.

MAJOR DIVISIONS of GEOLOGIC TIME

CENOZOIC ERA (Age of Recent Life)	Quaternary Period	The several geologic eras were originally named Primary, Secondary, Tertiary, and Quaternary. The first two names are no longer used; Tertiary and Quaternary have been retained but used as period designations.
	Tertiary Period	
MESOZOIC ERA (Age of Medieval Life)	Cretaceous Period	Derived from Latin word for chalk (creta) and first applied to extensive deposits that form white cliffs along the English Channel.
	Jurassic Period	Named for the Jura Mountains, located between France and Switzerland, where rocks of this age were first studied.
	Triassic Period	Taken from word "trias" in recognition of the threefold character of these rocks in Europe.
PALEOZOIC ERA (Age of Ancient Life)	Permian Period	Named after the province of Perm, U.S.S.R., where these rocks were first studied.
	Pennsylvanian Period	Named for the State of Pennsylvania where these rocks have produced much coal.
	Mississippian Period	Named for the Mississippi River valley where these rocks are well exposed.
	Devonian Period	Named after Devonshire County, England, where these rocks were first studied.
	Silurian Period	Named after Celtic tribes, the Silures and the Ordovices, that lived in Wales during the Roman Conquest.
	Ordovician Period	
	Cambrian Period	Taken from Roman name for Wales (Cambria) where rocks containing the earliest evidence of complex forms of life were first studied.
PRECAMBRIAN ERA	— — — — — — —	The time between the birth of the planet and the appearance of complex forms of life. More than 80 percent of the Earth's estimated 4½ billion years falls within this era.

Fig. 29-4 The geologic time scale. All rocks of the earth's crust, especially those containing fossils, can be placed conveniently in the framework of this scale. This version is based on information from the United States Geological Survey.

given a place for the operation of an all-powerful God. In the totality of time and eternity and by the boundless wisdom of God both are possible.

THE AGE OF THE EARTH

Some scholars have strongly supported the idea that a creation day is 1,000 years long. The chief basis for this belief is the reference to 1,000-year-long days in II Peter.

> But, beloved, be not ignorant of this one thing, that one day is with the Lord as a thousand years, and a thousand years as one day.
>
> II Peter 3:8

Again there would seem to be two possible interpretations. Both require the reader to supply what he considers to be the proper meaning. Those who would equate one day of God with a thousand years of man would have to supply the words in parenthesis—"that one day is with the Lord as a thousand years (with man) and a thousand years (with man) is as one day (with the Lord)." Those who might consider this verse merely as indicating that time has less meaning with God than with man would supply the following parenthetical words—"That one day with the Lord is as a thousand years (with the Lord) and a thousand years (with the Lord) is as one day (with the Lord)."

Another scripture to be considered is this:

> For a thousand years in thy sight is but as yesterday when it is past, and as a watch in the night.
>
> Psalm 90:4

Certainly the phrase "a thousand years" is frequently used to designate a long time period without a real intent to be specific. Thus even today we frequently hear such expressions as "never in a thousand years." Students of scripture are apparently free to decide whether or not the creative periods were 24-hours, 1,000 years, or indefinite periods of greater length. Evidently in ancient times the concept of great numbers and long time periods were conveyed well enough by the words thousand and thousands; these words are found in about 450 verses in the King James translation. The word millions, which is a commonplace expression today for largeness and greatness, is found once in the King James version; the word million occurs not at all.

COMMENTS AND REFERENCES

The seventh day is a reality of biblical literature. All commentaries give space to it but emphasis and approaches differ from church to church. Most references to the seventh day are related to the Sabbath or Sunday, how these are celebrated, which day of the week is the seventh day, and events associated with it in history. It is surprising that the institution of a day of rest as a memorial to the rest of God after the works of creation is usually barely mentioned, seldom stressed.

The attitude that the seventh day is more of a convenience for man or perhaps even his invention than it is a serious reminder about the creation seems widespread. The Sabbath has certainly become more human-oriented and less God-oriented. Many historical and legalistic connotations of the Sabbath receive much more attention than does any thought that it tells some very profound things about the natural world.

The problem of whether or not we are still in the seventh day seems of little concern to Bible students. In this book a central argument is that the seventh day is not over and that God's word is true and literal—he completed his creative works and has desisted from this type of effort since rains fell naturally upon the earth at the beginning of the seventh day a very long time ago.

Comments on the seventh day may be found in *The Interpreters Bible*, vol. 1, p. 488-490; *The Encyclopedia Judaica*, vol. 14, p. 558-573; *The New Catholic Encyclopedia*, vol. 12, p. 778-782; *The Catholic Encyclopedia*, vol. 4, p. 476-473; and *The Encyclopedia of Biblical Interpretation*, vol. 1, p. 78-86. The last named reference seems to express all possible thoughts on the subject. *Mormon Doctrine*, 1958 edition, p. 592 contains a brief entry on the sabbath.

... A MIST FROM THE EARTH ...
WATERED ... THE GROUND

But there went up a mist from the earth, and
watered the whole face of the ground.

Genesis 2:6

T he watering of the ground as described in the above verse
was a major turning point in the history of the earth. Apparently
it is the first event of the seventh day and with it begins the
"natural" existence of living things. Plants and animals could
now be assured of a permanent habitation.

This particular verse constitutes a most significant link
between science and scripture, between Genesis and geology.
Here we are told in a somewhat figurative but unmistakable way
that the waters came out of the earth. The presence of water on
the earth constitutes a great scientific problem. It is now fairly
certain that none of the other planets of the solar system possess
bodies of liquid water; the earth is unique in having abundant
oceans, lakes, ice caps and atmospheric clouds. About
300,000,000 cubic miles of liquid water exist on the surface of
the globe; incidentally it might well have been called Water and
not Earth.

Where did the earth get its water in the first place and how
has it been able to keep it for long periods of time? The answer
involves a great deal of technical information and speculation

that need not be given in detail here. Assume as an arbitrary starting point that the earth was once molten, completely melted from center to surface and of course so hot that there could be no solid crust, let alone bodies of water. In prescientific centuries it was assumed that all the water of the earth was once contained in a thick cloudy atmosphere. Under this theory any water that fell as rain would immediately evaporate and return to the clouds above. At this point we should note that only about 3,100 cubic miles of the earth's total water is in the atmosphere at any one time. The primitive atmosphere, if it really contained all the water now on the earth would have been incomparably more dense and extensive than the present one.

But the idea of all the water being in a primitive atmosphere is no longer in favor. A much better theory was proposed by the geologist R. R. Rubey in 1952. In brief terms his theory proposes that the water that now exists on or near the earth's surface came from within its interior. The appearance of water at the

Fig. 30-1   Water on the earth and in its heavens.
(Courtesy Utah Historical Society.)

surface was a direct consequence of cooling and solidification. The technical term for the process involved is "degassing"; this may be crudely compared to a stewing or cooking process. The essential elements for creating water are abundantly present within the earth perhaps in uncombined or disassociated form. This is shown by the continuous appearance of enormous quantities of water and water vapor from volcanoes, fumaroles, hot springs and geysers. All that is needed is plenty of time for enough water to come to the surface to fill the ocean basins and saturate the atmosphere. It is supposed that the rate of water production has been decreasing and that there was more volcanic action in the earlier stages of the earth's history.

Fig. 30-2 Artist's impression of the primitive earth in process of cooling from its molten state. Water is shown rising from the earth in the form of steam, accumulating in clouds, and returning to the surface as rain.

(From *Science News*, reproduced with permission.)

Fig. 30-3   Mists out of the earth. Water emerges continually from within the earth in the form of volcanic emanations, hot springs, geysers, and fumaroles. The upper photograph shows "smoke" (really mostly water vapor) rising from the crater of Mount Martin, Alaska. The lower photo is a geyser in Yellowstone Park, Wyoming.

(U.S. Park Service.)

Many lines of evidence indicate that Rubey's theory is at least on the right track. Common sense as well as good chemical theory tells us that a molten earth-sized body would be so hot that most gasses including water vapor would be driven into space and lost forever. To escape from the earth a molecule of water vapor would have to attain a velocity of almost 3,700 feet per second. This velocity could easily be reached in association with a molten earth. Here also is an explanation for the absence of water on the Moon and its scarcity on Mars. The escape velocity from the Moon is approximately 750 feet per second and is easily attained by any volatile material that is or has been there. Even though water may have been produced from the interior it would have escaped as soon as it appeared. Mars has an escape velocity of 1,600 feet per second and some water is retained. It is worth mentioning in passing that Jupiter has a layer or shell of water vapor in its atmosphere and water ice is probably present on Saturn.

The accumulation of water under the Rubey theory was a relatively slow process. This is significant in connection with the saltiness of the ocean. If one were to believe in the sudden production of the ocean as soon as rain could fall on a newly cooled earth it seems obvious that these water bodies would be relatively fresh. The salt would have to be added slowly as erosion of the land took place. The best evidence we have is that the oceans were salty from the beginning; as the water increased in volume salt was slowly added to keep the salinity about the same through time.

From the viewpoint of living things including man the most important event in the history of the earth was the appearance of water. Water in liquid form exists in exactly the same temperature range that living things can tolerate. This is only to be expected because protoplasm is about 80 percent water and the body of a land-living vertebrate is about 75 percent water. The presence of water anywhere indicates that the temperature is right for life. We wouldn't expect to find life as we know it on planets either too hot or too cold for liquid water.

Geologists recognize another important effect of water. This is its essential role in producing the sedimentary rock record. In

Fig. 30-4   Watery earth, waterless moon. The ever-changing cloud patterns of
the atmosphere, the surf lines where seas and oceans meet the land, the
waxing and waning of snow cover and the seasonal changes in vegetation as
seen in distant views of earth are impressive proofs of the presence of water.

   By contrast the static changeless surface of the moon marked by only
ancient unhealed impact scars and barren lava fields tells what a planet must
be without the influence of water.

(NASA.)

other words, the great class of rocks which results from deposition in water could not begin to form until water was present in large amounts. Igneous and metamorphic rocks were being formed from the beginning of the earth but not such water-laid varieties as sandstone, limestone, shale and coal. We can be assured that geologists can recognize the effects of water deposition in rocks of ancient origin. Such features as ripple marks, raindrop impressions, cross-bedding and concretions are sure accompaniments of water. Since most of these evidences require water in motion it is fairly certain that the same forces which now operate were operating then to lift water vapor into the

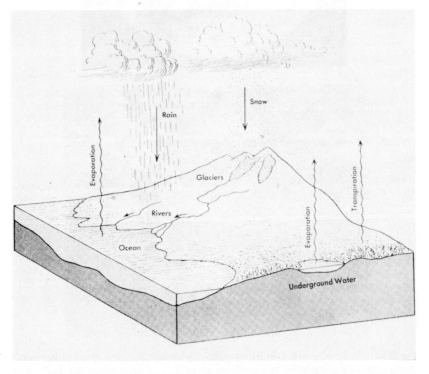

Fig. 30-5   The water cycle of the earth. The movement of water across the land and through the oceans and atmosphere assures all life a supply of dissolved nutrients and oxygen. Only about one hundred-thousandths of the total water of the globe is in the atmosphere at any one time. From William Lee Stokes, Sheldon Judson, and M. Dane Picard, *Introduction to Geology* (Englewood Cliffs, N.J.: Prentice-Hall, Inc., 1978), p. 204.

atmosphere and to cause its condensation and precipitation so that it could flow downward by gravity in streams toward permanent oceans and seas. This is the great hydrological or water cycle of the earth.

Important indeed was the appearance of water; without it life could not exist on Earth and the surface of the planet would resemble that of the Moon or Mars. It is not to be wondered that geologists are very interested in finding the oldest sedimentary rocks as a sign of water action. And it is likewise not unremarkable that it is in these very old rocks that the first evidences of earth life are found.

The earliest known water-laid sediments are dated at about three billion five hundred million years old. These ancient rocks are the Fig Tree Series found in South Africa. Although other sedimentary rocks older than these may yet be found it is pointed out by geologists that few areas of the earth remain to be explored where such old rocks could be located.

Here is the important scriptural connection. If the watering of the earth took place over three billion years ago and we are still in the seventh day then the seventh day is already over 3

Fig. 30-6   "Fossil" ripple marks preserved in fine-grained sedimentary rock that was once mud in a shallow seaway of central Utah.
(U.S. Geological Survey.)

billion years long. Presumably this final day will close with the "end of the earth" at some indefinite time in the future. This raises the interesting problem of whether or not there are more than seven days in God's plans concerning this earth.

COMMENTS AND REFERENCES

This chapter deals specifically with the origin of the surface water of the earth. The very important paper by W. W. Rubey to which reference is made in the text is: Geologic history of sea water: an attempt to state the problem: *Geological Society of America Bulletin*, vol. 62, p. 1111-1147, 1951. A follow-up paper in the same technical vein is by H. D. Holland, 1972, The geologic history of sea water—an attempt to solve the problem, *Geochimica et Cosmochimica Acta*, vol. 36, p. 637-651.

An excellent book on the origin of water and related topics is: P. J. Brancazio and A. G. W. Cameron (eds.), 1964, *The Origin and Evolution of Atmosphere and Oceans*, John Wiley and Sons. Also up-to-date and informative is James C. G. Walker, 1977, *Evolution of the Atmosphere*, Macmillan Publishing Co.

Water as a substance essential to life is discussed in a non-technical way in the Yearbook of the U.S. Department of Agriculture for 1955. Titled simply *Water*, this book shows the vital influence of water in human affairs. A popular prize-winning discussion of the greatest water body of earth is Rachel L. Carson, 1961, *The Sea Around Us* (rev. ed.), Oxford University Press.

"Evolution describes how God loved Man (human beings) into existence."

... OF ... DUST ... THE BREATH OF LIFE ... MAN BECAME A LIVING SOUL

> And the Lord God formed man of the dust of the ground, and breathed into his nostrils the breath of life; and man became a living soul.
>
> Genesis 2:7

No single subject has so baffled and frustrated man as his attempts to define himself. Is he an exalted beast or a fallen angel? The Psalmist asks: What is man . . . ? And there must be at least part of an answer in Paul's first epistle to the Corinthians:

> . . . There is a natural body, and there is a spiritual body.
>
> And so it is written, The first man Adam was made a living soul; and the last Adam was made a quickening spirit.
>
> Howbeit that was not first which is spiritual, but that which is natural; and afterward that which is spiritual.
>
> The first man is of the earth, earthy: the second man is the Lord from heaven.
>
> 1 Corinthians 15:44-47

The creation scripture gives two accounts of the coming forth of man. The texts which open this chapter describe the appearance of the specific Adam on the seventh day. It may be well to recall for comparison and contrast what is said in the account of the previous or sixth day. This describes the preparations for man and speaks of him in a general way only:

> So God created man in his own image, in the image of God created he him; male and female created he them.
>
> Genesis 1:27

The sixth-day description is important and revealing but it is the seventh day narrative that is of concern at this point. Here, the dual nature of man is implied: there is a physical man, the entity formed from the dust of the ground and a spiritual man, the spirit that was put into the physical body so that the totality became a living soul.

Fig. 31-1   . . . God hath made man upright . . . (Ecclesiastes 7:29). ►

Man rises above the beasts for many reasons. His superior intellect and immortal soul are of undeniable importance but are difficult to weigh and measure in scientific terms. An upright posture is no less important; and any person, with a little observation of his or her own body, can be convinced why this is so. Humans are erect chiefly because their weight is balanced on the two hind limbs and these are also suited to carrying out the function of locomotion. Another important consequence of an erect posture is that the head with the all-important brain, sense organs and jaws can be supported on a short neck and moved with very little expenditure of energy.

Humans have a relatively large number of rather simple teeth. The shape of the face conforms to the uses to which the teeth are put and is much less beastial than other animals because sharp tearing, cutting, and piercing teeth essential to fighting and food gathering are not necessary and the jaws are correspondingly shortened. It seems that in humans the brain has assumed supremacy over the teeth; the cranium, neatly balanced on the spinal column, pushes forward to overshadow the face, giving a profile totally unlike that of the other mammals.

The forelimbs have been freed from weight-bearing and locomotion and have become the chief servants of the brain in accomplishing thousands of essentially human tasks. One of the chief functions of the flexible arms and agile hands is the procurement and transfer of food from the source to the mouth. In most animals the head, neck, and frequently the entire body must be moved in feeding. And speaking of diet, man is not dependent on any particular food; he is not only the world's most effective biped he is its most versatile omnivore. Humans have escaped being over-specialized in many other ways. They can run, crawl, climb, and swim with only moderate efficiency and are not dependent on any one mode of life or place of existence.

So far as his physical body, built upon an upright frame, is concerned, man is sufficiently well endowed to subdue the earth and take dominion over all other living things.

(Courtesy of the American Museum of Natural History.)

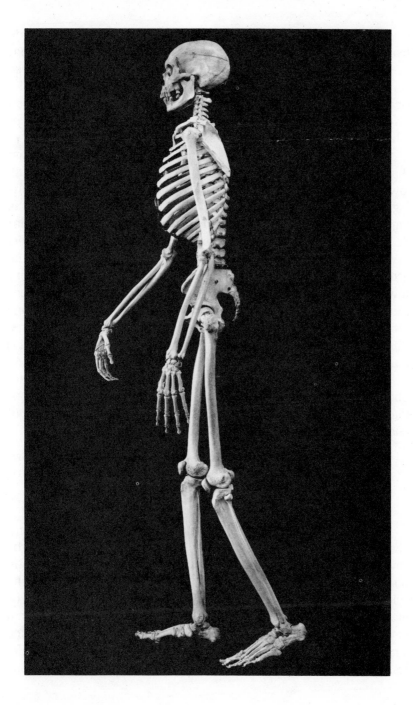

Consider the origin of the body of man—the entity made from the dust on the seventh day. It is somewhat surprising that the familiar phrase "dust of the earth" is not found in these scriptures—instead all use the phrase "dust of the ground." Ground seems to be a better word than earth because as used elsewhere in Genesis it conveys a very good mental image of what men and living things generally are really made of.

Note the usage of Genesis 2:6 which describes the mist that ". . . watered the whole face of the ground." This is followed immediately by the planting of the garden of Eden, implying, it would seem, that it is the soil that men cultivate that is important here. And we are informed very soon in verse 9 that ". . . out of the ground made the Lord God to grow every tree. . . ." And not much later as told in verse 19, "And out of the ground the Lord God formed every beast of the field, and every fowl of the air. . . ." There are many other scriptural references to both ground and earth; but when growing plants and living animals are being discussed it is usually in terms of the ground, thus: ". . . cursed is the ground for thy sake . . ." (Genesis 3:17) and ". . . but Cain was a tiller of the ground. . . ." (Genesis 4:2.)

Usage of the term ground emphasizes a basic unifying fact about the physical (not spiritual) origin of all earthly beings. Plants, animals, and even man are described as being made of one common material. And finally this sobering thought:

> In the sweat of thy face shalt thou eat bread, till thou return unto the ground; for out of it wast thou taken; for dust thou art, and unto dust shalt thou return.
>
> Genesis 3:19

No other phraseology gives such perfect opportunity for a choice between the figurative and the literal. It might even be said that here one is forced to choose between the mystical earthbound thinking of ancient times and the precise thinking of the scientific present. It was not difficult for men of ancient or medieval times to imagine the bringing forth of man as a magical or supernatural act. Artists represented the event time and time again as the instantaneous transformation of an inert and lifeless image of a man into a perfect, living person. Comparisons were based on common experience such as the shaping of vessels by the village potter. That God should do the shaping seems to be required by scriptural authority; God is the one who made man and animals. The most logical way to make anything is with one's hands.

> But now, O Lord, thou art our father; we are the clay, and thou our potter; and we all are the work of thy hand.
>
> Isaiah 65:8

The picture of God literally shaping man with his hands as a potter shapes his clay is beautiful and impressive imagery suitable and irreproachable for a more innocent age. But with the passage of time the image of the Great Potter has faded and other interpretations have emerged. Man is still seen as being made of the dust but in a more indirect and complicated way. How dust, ground, clay, or soil become living tissue is studied today in numerous technical fields including biochemistry, nutrition, and physiology. And how to manage the dust of the earth so as to make it productive and keep our own allotment of clay alive has become a major problem of mankind.

Modern science has made clear the successive steps required in the conversion of the raw materials of the earth into muscle, eye and brain. Much of the magic has faded but the wonder is no less. And what has this modern knowledge done to the creation story? To some it has revealed the Genesis account as a fable made up by and for the superstitious and ignorant. Others, more tolerant of the seeming childishness of an earlier age, have substituted their own latter-day interpretation. The making of living things from the dust of the ground is no less significant to them than would be the infusion of life into a statue of stone. They see God not as a Great Potter but as a Great Chemist. To this group God must still be there, weighing and measuring as it were the proper combination of things to bring life and individuality to each of his numerous creations. Since each kind is different, each has its own recipe, its own formula, its own genetic code and its own time of creation. It is very special indeed, hence the idea of special creation. This is the way today's creationists view it—they recognize a divine miracle while admitting most of the assertions of science. What they do demand is the immanent presence and agency of God in bringing forth all life. To them any other view is intolerable and irreverent.

Evolutionists, by contrast, believe that the power of shaping the individual and of producing the species lies in the genes. In the genes, they see in capsule form the accumulated outcome of ages of trial and error together with mechanisms for transmitting this vital information and of improving on it. This view obviously does not require the presence of God at the creation of every new kind of life. In fact, it may not require his assistance even at the birth of the first life. Persons who follow this line of thinking are clearly at odds with traditional views of the creation and with contemporary creationism. Since evolutionists seem to have eliminated the necessity for God in creating the species they are accused of eliminating him altogether. This accusation is accepted without shame, guilt or remorse by many who would rather believe in no God at all than one who is impotent, ridiculous or unnecessary.

Many, if not most, informed persons brought up in the Judeo-Christian tradition find themselves caught between the extremes of creationism and evolutionism. These are in the main religious men and women who want to believe the Bible and will fight to defend it. To them the findings of science no matter how logical are dangerous and faith-destroying. If the public polls are to be believed the present is a time of return to the Bible. The greatest resurgence of belief is among the evangelical and fundamentalist sects many of which profess to accept scripture as literally true. It seems paradoxical that this return to the Bible comes at a time when space explorations and great discoveries in biology and geology make literal interpretations more difficult than ever before.

Obviously, millions of persons must be disregarding the problem while others may be striving privately to make up their minds. The attitude that religion is in conflict with science and science is wrong is fortified by many Christian clergymen. Unfortunately these leaders seem to offer their followers only the alternatives of creationism or evolutionism. Scientists, in the main, appear unperturbed. To them the problem of the appearance and proliferation of species has been solved in favor of evolution. Any further argument is a waste of time; if the Bible conflicts with science it is the Bible that must give way. Certainly not to be overlooked are those dissident scientists who profess full belief in the scripture but do not go along with their colleagues on such subjects as the age of the earth and organic evolution. Some of these belong to the Creation Research Society, others may share the same views but are not formally affiliated with the Society.

There is one more group and it may be the smallest of all. Its members profess to believe in God but do not wish to be called creationists in the sense that the term is currently applied. They have had to abandon traditional scriptural interpretations and are therefore regarded with hostility by their theological contemporaries and with a degree of disdain by their scientific colleagues. Time will tell whether a place can be found for this minority.

MAN AND ANIMALS

Man, in spite of his importance, did not have a day of creation that was exclusively his own. According to scripture he entered the scene on the sixth day preceded by other land-living animals in great variety. The relationship of men and animals has been a most puzzling one for thinkers throughout the ages. No matter what view one may have of the origin of man the presence of other beings that resemble him in various degrees is a fact to be dealt with in all seriousness.

In some societies animals are called brothers and treated accordingly. In fables beyond number the beasts are given the attributes of human speech, thought, and action. Animals have been variously worshipped as gods, regarded with fear and superstition, hunted to extinction, domesticated for food and kept as intimate pets or valued servants. Obviously they can be cast in no simple role.

It would be foolish to deny that in the prescientific ages man felt and made abundantly manifest a close kinship with the animals. In many societies the status of man was exactly that of an animal—he being different not so much in kind as in degree from his associates of the forests and plains. With the scientific age, zoology and comparative anatomy began to look at living things in objective ways with the conclusion that man is officially classed as an animal.

Furthermore he is a chordate (has a dorsal nervous system), a vertebrate (backbone), a mammal (hair, milk), a primate (5 fingers, 32 teeth, stereoscopic vision) and finally a homonoid (large brain, erect posture, even row of teeth).

Although the zoological assignment of man among the animals seems well founded and unarguable, reactions to it have ranged from bitter outrage through weary resignation, to gladsome relief.

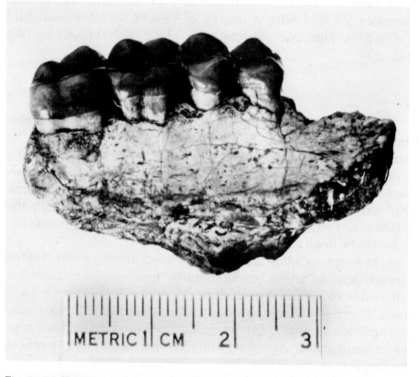

Fig. 31-2   Human or not human? Fossil teeth such as this constitute much of the basic evidence of ancient humans and non humans.
(Courtesy Elwyn Simons.)

In spite of the fact that science places man in the highest category of the animal world this is not good enough for most of us. We want a separate more exalted position. We shudder at the sight of what science declares to be our distant living relatives, the apes, and are repelled by the fossilized remains of the still closer kinfolk that scientists have disinterred from the earth. Many sternly disavow any relationship with the rest of creation and place heavy blame upon science for classifying man as an animal related to the monkeys. But a kinship is too obvious; man like the other animals must eat to live; his body functions are disgustingly beastial, his methods of reproduction are no better than those of the monkeys, he is born in blood and water, he suffers, dies and decays like all flesh. In the face of all his earthly trappings how can he in good conscience place himself above the animal creation? In their more reflective moments some may wonder why God made man so much like the monkey or vice versa. Should not the crown of creation be something more special, more glorious, more godlike in its form and functions? Is the distinction no more than that implied by the title of a popular book, *The Naked Ape*?

What do scriptures have to say about the relationship of man and the other animals? Creationists are fond of pointing out that God *made* the beasts of the earth and cattle and creeping things but that he *created* man from the dust of the earth in his own image, inferring that there could be no evolutionary connection between man and any lower creations. But the way is left open for such a connection and why it is neither specifically denied or affirmed must remain a matter of individual speculation.

Consider these similarities in the description of the coming forth of man and of animals:

(a) Both are made from the dust of the ground.

And the Lord God formed man of the dust of the ground.

Genesis 2:7

And out of the ground the Lord God formed every beast of the field and every fowl of the air.

Genesis 2:19

(b) Both are to exist by the same means:

... Behold, I have given you (man) every herb bearing seed ... every tree ... *to you it shall be for meant.*

Genesis 1:29

And to every beast of the earth, and every fowl of the air, and to every thing that creepeth upon the earth, wherein there is life, *I have given every green herb for meat.*

Genesis 1:30

Where then is there a difference between man and animal that can be defended by the creation scripture? In the last analysis it is in his assigned status as much as in his indicated origin that man is clearly given a position superior to animals. God did not exactly command man to assume dominion but the meaning is unmistakable: "and have dominion over the fish of the sea, and over the fowl of the air, and over every living thing that moveth upon the earth." (Genesis 1:28.) Later Adam gave names to the beasts of the field and fowl of the air an act proving his superiority over them.

Theologians seem unable or unwilling to agree on a specific description of how man's physical body came into being. To say that it was miraculous or supernatural in this day of scientific inquiry is not enough. Science has at least provided a theory as to how physical man could have originated and is steadily accumulating evidence to support it. But theologians have mostly condemned the theory of organic evolution in such horrifying terms that the average Christian is convinced that it is not only erroneous but evil and dangerous.

As to the origin of the spirit of man things are even more uncertain. It is a subject on which science naturally is silent. Here, where theology might be expected to make one of its greatest contributions, there are deep-seated differences of opinion. The time, place and manner of creation of the spirit remain clouded in mystery.

It seems scarcely fair that science should be condemned for not proving a divine origin for the body of man when theology has trouble explaining the origin of the spirit. It is doubtful that

Fig. 31-3   God creating Eve from Adam's side. That this was a final creative act is shown by the presence of plants and animals on land, fish in the sea, birds in the air and sun, moon, and stars in the heavens. From a woodcut published in 1614.

science can do more than it has already done to dignify man. By any standard which measures success and eminence man is the crowning glory of creation. He has not only survived but has achieved dominance over all other living things. To zoologists man occupies the highest tip of the highest branch of the tree of life. Those who classify animals regard man as constituting an entire species, genus, and family; he has, in other words, no close living relatives.

Theologians evidently want scientists to admit the possibility of a supernatural origin for man's body. On the other hand scientists are asking theologians to agree that a natural origin might be possible. That either side should give ground seems unlikely. Science has succeeded only when it has cast off any and all appeals to the supernatural. If theologians were to admit that man has evolved they fear the danger of downgrading or eliminating God as the creator. Few on either side can perceive that evolution is a great creative process that dignifies man and glorifies God. Meanwhile, until reason prevails over pride and prejudice, the common man must struggle to reconcile his two opposing natures as best he can.

COMMENTS AND REFERENCES

No one denies that man has been around for at least several thousand years. Some think he arrived fully developed at a relatively late date to take command of a world already prepared for him. Others say his roots go back billions of years and that he evolved along with the earth and other forms of life. Those who believe in his supernatural origin base their case chiefly on the Genesis account which states that man is a creation of God. What this phrase means is at the core of the argument between creationists and evolutionists.

It is not the purpose of this book to try to convince anyone that they should become either creationists or evolutionists. If a person has accepted the explanations offered for pre-human events he or she may be willing to abandon strict literal meanings and find naturalistic explanations not too objectionable. The literature on human origins is immense and has been written almost entirely by persons whose minds are already made up and who do not wish to contend over issues they consider to have been settled decades ago. Recent discussions of human origins are, I believe, more candid and less emotional than at any previous time. The problem as seen by scientists is not did man evolve, but rather how, where, and why did he evolve. A selection of recent titles such as given below illustrates the trend today: Ian Tattersall and Niles Eldridge, 1977, Fact, theory, and fantasy in human paleontology: in *American Scientist*, vol. 65, no. 2; R. E. F. Leakey, 1976, Hominids in Africa: in *American Scientist*, vol. 64, no. 2; Richard G. Klein, 1977, The ecology of early man in Southern Africa: in *Science*, vol. 197, no. 4299; Gina Bari Kolata, 1977, Human evolution: in *Science*, vol. 197, no. 4300; Henry M. McHenry, 1975, Fossils and the mosaic nature of human evolution: in *Science*, vol. 190, no. 4213; David Pilbeam and S. J. Gould, 1974, Size and scaling in human evolution: in *Science*, vol. 186, no. 4167; Robert B. Eckhardt, 1972, Population genetics and human origins, in *Scientific American*, vol. 226, no. 1; Gina Bari Kotata, 1975, Human evolution; life-styles and lineages of early hominids: in *Science*, vol. 178, no. 4180; Laura Evans, 1972, Ancestral Secrets: in *The Sciences*, vol. 12, no. 3.

References such as these might be multiplied endlessly and searched with scant solace by those who cannot accept evolutionary concepts. Practically nothing in present-day science writing will be found that argues against the evolution of man. But all sides deserve to be heard. The fact of growing opposition to evolution has been mentioned in references to preceding chapters. A number of books, study guides, films, and newsletters are available from the Creation Research Society.

POSTSCRIPT

Between the time I commenced to write this book and the completion of the printer's proof three important books appeared on the market. These are: Jastrow, Robert, *God and the Astronomers*, New York and London: W. W. Norton, 1978; Sagan, Carl, *Cosmos*, New York: Random House, 1980; and Asimov, Isaac, *In the Beginning*, New York: Crown Publishers, 1981.

These books and mine have one thing in common, they deal with the origin of things. *God and the Astronomers* makes one chief point: the assertion of Genesis that there was a specific beginning is mirrored in the big bang scientific theory of the universe. Robert Jastrow, an astronomer, narrates the conception and verification of the theory and brings to life the personalities who contributed to it.

Cosmos has been on the best-seller list for a phenomenal 43 weeks as of September, 1981. It summarizes the discoveries of science and comments on the individuals who led mankind from intellectual darkness into the space age. Carl Sagan, also an astronomer, had drawn upon his exceptional knowledge of many sciences and on material assembled for his popular thirteen-part multimillion-dollar television series.

In the Beginning has been advertised as the most important of Isaac Asimov's 220 books. It is a factual unemotional comparison of the biblical and scientific stories of creation. Asimov carefully analyzes individual words and phrases of the creation scriptures and compares his concept of their meaning with the established facts and well-founded inferences of science.

I must thank these writers for literally paving the way for my book. Jastrow has established the first pier of the bridge that must eventually unite science and religion. He has found solid meaning in the first verse of Genesis; I hope to have established many additional piers on subsequent verses. Sagan presents thousands of facts and scores of great illustrations that explain in layman's terms the nature of the known universe. Without the discoveries of the space age, so well described by Sagan, my book could never have been written. Nothing in *Cosmos*, contradicts my book; our scientific subject matter is the same.

My greatest debt is to Isaac Asimov. He has shown in a decisive way the difficulties of defending traditional interpretations of the biblical creation scriptures. This is exactly what I have tried to do. In any conflict of ideas, erroneous concepts must be proven wrong before substitutes can gain attention and credibility.

These books cannot be ignored by Bible believers. It matters not that they are true and factual and that they are the products of trained analytical minds; they will be criticized because they do not give credit to the scriptures as the literal and infallible words of the creator God. This is unfortunate because the vast majority of Bible believers will not understand the faith-promoting value of that which science has discovered. In a most important way these books are essential steps in the right direction.

Cosmos mixes fact and speculation in a way that clearly appeals to multitudes of readers. Its popularity is not based on religious content; words such as God, Genesis, Moses and scripture are not found in the index. I cannot fault Sagan for this; *Cosmos* is not antireligious, rather it is areligious. Readers are free to draw their own faith-promoting or faith-destroying conclusions from what it contains. Jastrow highlights God in the title of his book and the text has many religious overtones. However, the book fails as an effective defense of Genesis; and since there is no intimation that the author believes in creationism, it too will be criticized as lukewarm, incomplete and self-defeating.

Asimov's contribution is something else again. His methods are scholarly, his logic sound and his conclusions well founded. However, Bible believers should note and take comfort in the thought that Asimov begins with the assumption, made perfectly plain in his introduction, that Genesis is strictly a human document. The subtitle of *In the Beginning* reads "Science Faces God in the Book of Genesis." Small wonder that under Asimov's rules God loses in the confrontation.

My egotistical hope is that *The Genesis Code* might become a religious man's *Cosmos* and a believer's alternative to *In the Beginning.*

INDEX

Numerals in italic refer to illustrations.